A BOOK OF PRAISES

A Workbook on the Psalms

Dermot Connolly

VERITAS

ACKNOWLEDGEMENTS

One thing that becomes clear when you study the Psalms is that many people had a hand in their making; and the fact that someone's name appears at the head of a psalm is no guarantee that he is its sole author. Much the same could be said of this book.

It has grown out of a course we did in 1982 in the Bible Study Group at St Mary's Church, Ajegunle, Lagos. Since that year the course was developed, and once again the same group — with new members — went through every page and every exercise. The final work is the product of that experience. I cannot adequately express my thanks to the Ajegunle Group for all they have taught me over the years we have shared the Psalms together. It is a mixed group — men and women, young and old — with a remarkable sensitivity to the spirit and truth of the Scriptures.

Among many other people who have encouraged and guided me, three in particular have contributed to the writing of this book. Especially in the early days, when I was first considering the task, Sr Majella McCarron OLA was a wise, gentle but unrelenting guide. 'Keep it simple!' she said — but that is the most difficult thing of all, and I'm not sure I have often succeeded. Fr Maurice Kelly, my colleague at St Mary's at the time, has been a good friend not only in reading, correcting and especially advising on the manuscript, but also in taking up more than his fair share of the work whenever I was away writing. Above all, Sr Maura Ramsbottom, MMM, who has contributed to the soul of this book. As well as her own personal insights on the Psalms, she brought the reflections of a mixed group of novices with whom she did almost all of this course.

My greatest debt of gratitude is the oldest, going back a quarter of a century to the two men who first opened the Scriptures for me, Fr Paddy Hannon and an tAth. Tomás Ó Curraoin, both of St Patrick's Missionary Society. This book is not worthy of them, and in the way of the true scholars that they are, they might not agree with everything in it. But it seems to me the most suitable way of saying my thanks to them.

Dermot Connolly
Ajegunle, Easter 1987

INTRODUCTION

This is a workbook on the Psalms; it is designed primarily for Bible study groups, though it can, of course, also be used for individual study. This is a *workbook*: it is not intended to be an everlasting work of reference — there are other more comprehensive and more enduring books than this on the Psalms! What I have tried to do is produce a course of study on the Psalms and their background, with exercises, discussion topics, and questions to help the readers explore for themselves the riches of these prayer-songs, and to situate them in their own lives. Not all of the 150 Psalms in the Bible are dealt with directly in this course, but those found here are a representative group. Almost a third of the Psalms are reproduced in full (in the *Grail* translation) as well as parts of many other psalms and other passages from the Bible.

The key to appreciating the Psalms lies in understanding their *context* — or, rather, their many contexts. The experience of individuals, the story of the people of God, the worship of the community in the Jerusalem Temple, the searching of the early Christians, our own experience of life today — the Psalms find a living in all these different settings. It is my hope that this workbook may help us to know these various contexts, and so contribute to our appreciating the Psalms today.

Exercise 1:   *Yet another context of the Psalms is the Bible, the book itself. Written originally in Hebrew, Aramaic and Greek, the Bible has been translated into many of the world's languages. Each version has its own 'geography', and it is good to know your way around whatever version you are using. The following check-list may help you to Know Your Bible.*

What version is your bible?
   Authorised Version (King James) (*AV*)
   Revised Standard Version (*RSV*)
   Jerusalem Bible (*JB*)
   New Jerusalem Bible (*NJB*)
   Today's English Version (*Good News*) (*TEV*)
   New English Bible (*NEB*)
   New American Bible (*NAB*)
   Grail (Psalms only)
   Other:

Does your bible have notes? (These may be at
the bottom of each page, or somewhere at
the end of the book.)

Does your bible have introductions to the
various books?

Are there maps in your bible?

Does it have notes or a chart of bible history?

Find the following books in your bible: *Page:*
   Leviticus
   Second Book of Samuel
   Judith
   Psalms
   Wisdom
   Hosea
   Matthew
   Revelation (or Apocalypse)

In answering the last part of Exercise 1 *you may have found that the books of* Judith *and* Wisdom *are not in the version of the Bible you are using. They belong to a group of Old Testament books that were written originally in Greek only; Bible translations that are based exclusively on the Hebrew original may not include them. Others in this group are* Tobit, I *and* II Maccabees, Sirach *(known also as* Ecclesiasticus*), Baruch, and some parts of the book of* Daniel.

In this book the usual English translation I use for the Psalms is the *Grail* version, and for all other parts of the Bible, the *New Jerusalem Bible*. In any study group there will usually be a number of different translations in use. This can cause some difficulties, and it may be helpful if the members of the group could agree on a common version, at least for the Psalms. I would suggest *The Psalms: Singing Version*, by the *Grail*, publihsed in Fount Paperback (Collins), if it is available. On the other hand, each translation has its own merits, and it can be an enriching experience to listen to a psalm read in a variety of translations.

The course begins with an introduction to the Psalms, a chapter that might be called 'How the Psalms Work' — how they were written and why, how they were collected and used later on, how *we* might pray with them. The rest of the course deals with various contexts or settings in which the Psalms were written, and similar settings in our lives today: the story of the people of Israel and our story; the city of Jerusalem and worship in the Temple there — and worship now; how the Israelites saw creation and the world around them, and how Christians see the world; Kings and rulers then and now; and the mystery of God. So the course is constantly moving from the world of the Bible to our world and back, from life to the Psalms and back to life again.

How to find and refer to particular passages in the Bible

From the brief description I have given of this study course it is clear that we will be ranging up and down the Bible. Almost every book in the Bible is divided into *chapters*, and each chapter is divided into *verses*. This makes it very easy to pinpoint a particular passage or verse in any book of the Bible. For example, David's lament at the death of Saul and Jonathan is to be found in the Second Book of Samuel, chapter one, verses seventeen to twenty seven, or *2 Samuel 1:17-27*. The parable of the Prodigal Son can be read in the Gospel according to St Luke, chapter 15, verses 11 to 32, or *Luke 15:11-32*.

Occasionally reference has to be made to a passage that runs over from one chapter to another. The Passion and Death of Jesus, from the agony in the garden to his burial, are described in the Gospel according to St Matthew, chapter twenty-six, from verse thirty-six to the end, and chapter twenty-seven in its entirety, or *Matthew 26:36-27:66* (verse 66 being the final verse in chapter 27).

As you can see, what we have here is a kind of shorthand for easy reference to any part of the Bible. It just needs a little practice to be able to use it easily. Perhaps the most important thing is to *know your Bible*! — to be able to find any book of the Old or New Testament quickly and easily.

Exercise 2:   *What do you find at the following references?*

Exodus 20: 1-17
1 Kings 18:20-40
Psalm 23
Matthew 13:33
Acts of Apostles 20:17-38

A note on numbers: Shortly before 250 BC, the Hebrew scriptures were translated into Greek in a version known as the *Septuagint* (referring to the Greek number 70: there was a tradition that seventy scribes were involved in the work of translation). During the course of this translating some minor changes were made: Psalms 9 and 10 were joined together, as were Psalms 114 and 115. On the other hand, the Hebrew versions of both Psalms 116 and 147 were divided in two. The result was a difference in the numbering of the psalms in the Hebrew and Greek versions. As a general rule, from Psalm 10 to Psalm 148 the numbering of the Hebrew is one higher than the Greek, e.g. Psalm 57 in Hebrew is Psalm 56 in Greek.

This difference was carried over into modern translations also. Most follow the Hebrew system (RSV, JB, TEV, NAB etc) but some follow the Greek system, the *Grail* version being one of them (along with many of the liturgical books, missals and lectionaries in the Catholic Church). This difference in numbering is not of any importance, but it can cause endless confusion. In this workbook, it is the *Hebrew system* that is used, even when referring to the *Grail* translation.

How to use this book:

In a sense, you can use this book any way you like. The sequence of chapters can be changed without too much distortion of the course; you might, for instance, wish to take a break in Chapter 1 after section 1.3, and go on to the Story in Chapter 2. And you will certainly be able to devise more and better exercises than I have given. I have made no effort to produce 'class-length' units in this course, that is units that are intended to be completed within a single class period. I believe a Bible study group should be free to move as slowly and as easily as it wishes through a course such as this, and be able to 'stop where you find fruit!' as the old advice has it. The sequence of 'study' could be interspersed with sessions of prayer and meditation. The group could perhaps be moved to apostolic action. At all times, be open to the Spirit!

How much 'homework' can or need be done will depend on the group: some people like to do all the work together in the meeting, others like to do private work as well. The leader will need to discover the best way for his particular group. Above all, it is vital for the *leader* at least to be well-prepared for the group meetings. Good preparation for such meetings is, in fact, an aspect of being docile to the Spirit.

1 THE MAKING OF THE BOOK

In this first chapter we will be trying to answer such questions as: Who wrote the Psalms? Why were they written? How were they used, and who used them? Are all the Psalms the same, or are there different kinds of psalm? How were they gathered together, and why? These, and other such questions, are not really concerned with the *meaning* and *message* of the Psalms, the story that they tell; rather are they examining the story of the Book of Psalms itself.

1.1   THE LIFE SITUATIONS OF THE PSALMS

The single most important thing to realise about the Psalms is that they are all based on real situations in real life. They refer to experiences either in the life of an individual or in the story of the People of Israel. If we want to understand a psalm we must try to discover what condition or event lies behind it. For example:

> *Psalm 71*
> The prayer of an old man who is in danger from 'the hand of the wicked, from the grip of the unjust, of the oppressor' (*v 4*). He has put his trust in God since his youth ('On you I have leaned from my birth, from my mother's womb you have been my help' (*v 6*). Now his prayer is that God will remember him in his old age: 'Now that I am old and grey-headed, do not forsake me, God' (*v 8*).

> *Psalm 79*
> A cry of outrage against the destruction of the holy city of Jerusalem. A harrowing description of the enemy's assault (*vv 1-4*) is followed by a plea for help: 'Let your compassion hasten to meet us, we are left in the depths of distress' (*v 8*).

By careful reading of the psalm we can know what kind of life-situation lay behind it — a situation of need or joy or praise or desire, talk of travel or enemies or sickness or Jerusalem. It is possible that the psalmist composed his song in the very situation itself, but it is more probable it was written at a later time of reflection on all that had happened. Whatever the case, the psalm was grounded in the life and history of the psalmist and his people.

Exercise 3:   *Can you suggest the life situations that produced the following psalms?*

   Psalm 38 (note vv 3-5)

   Psalm 70 (note vv 2-5)

   Psalm 122 (note vv 1-2)

   Psalm 138 (note v 3)

In a world that has many troubles, one of the most common types of psalm is the song of sorrow, the cry for help, the lament over some disaster, personal or national. For example:

Psalm 13

A plea for help against enemies. The psalmist's anguish is increased by the fear that God has forgotten him: 'How long, O Lord, will you forget me? How long will you hide your face?' (*v 1*).

Psalm 69

Again, the psalmist cries desperately for deliverance from his enemies: 'More numerous than the hairs on my head are those who hate me without cause' (*v 4*). They surround him like water; he is drowning in their hatred (*vv 1-2, 13-14*). He curses them bitterly (*vv 22-28*) and praises God in whom he places all his trust (*vv 30-36*).

Psalm 74

A sustained prayer of sorrow because of the destruction of Jerusalem and the Temple: 'Turn your steps to these places that are utterly ruined! The enemy has laid waste the whole of the sanctuary.' (*v 3*).

Exercise 4:   *In the following psalms of sorrow, can you suggest the cause of the psalmist's grief?*

Psalm 51 (note vv 3-5)

Psalm 55 (note vv 11-14)

Psalm 102

Psalm 137 (note vv 3-4)

Are there comparable situations in our lives when we might pray one of these psalms?

These psalms of sorrow arise out of situations of need in the life of the psalmist, needs that call to God for help. And when God does help, the singer is able to testify to that, to share the good news with his friends. And this gives rise to another situation in life, where the singer gives a testimony of his own personal experience of the goodness of God. Psalm 116A (114 in *Grail*) is an example of one such sharing.

Psalm 116A (114)   Song of a man saved from death

1. Alleluia!
   I love the Lord for he has heard
   the cry of my appeal;

   The singer introduces the theme of his song:

2. for he turned his ear to me
   in the day when I called him.

   God helped him in his time of need.

3. They surrounded me, the snares of death,
   with the anguish of the tomb;
   they caught me, sorrow and distress.

   He tells the tale to his friends

4. I called on the Lord's name.

   O Lord my God, deliver me!

5. How gracious is the Lord, and just;
   our God has compassion.

6. The Lord protects the simple hearts;
   I was helpless so he saved me.

7. Turn back, my soul, to your rest
   for the Lord has been good;

   A prayer of thanksgiving and hope

5

8. he has kept my soul from death,
   my eyes from tears
   and my feet from stumbling.
9. I will walk in the presence of the Lord
   in the land of the living.

The life-situation of this psalm is not only the experience of danger in the psalmist's life, but also his desire to share his story with his friends. There is a similar situation reflected in Psalm 30:

Psalm 30   The singer praises God and invites his friends to join in praise.

1. I will praise you, Lord, you have rescued me
   and have not let my enemies rejoice over me.
2. O Lord, I cried to you for help
   and you my God, have healed me.
3. O Lord, you have raised my soul from the dead,
   restored me to life from those who sink into
      the grave.

Addressed to God:
You are a God who saves!

4. Sing psalms to the Lord, you who love him,
   give thanks to his holy name.
5. His anger lasts but a moment; his favour through
      life.
   At night there are tears, but joy comes with dawn.
6. I said to myself in my good fortune:
   'Nothing will ever disturb me.'
7. Your favour had set me on a mountain fastness,
   then you hid your face and I was put to confusion.
8. To you, Lord, I cried,
   to my God I made appeal:
9. 'What profit would my death be, my going to
      the grave?
   Can dust give you praise or proclaim your truth?'
10. The Lord listened and had pity.
    The Lord came to my help.

Addressed to the
community: praise God for
his kindness
The psalmist's experience

11. For me you have changed my mourning into dancing,
    you removed my sackcloth and clothed me with joy.
12. So my soul sings psalms to you unceasingly.
    O Lord, my God, I will thank you for ever.

Addressed to God:
praise and thanksgiving

In Psalm 30 a song of trust and thanksgiving (vv 1-3, 11-12) surrounds a call to the community to praise God (vv 4-5) and a testimony to God's goodness in the psalmist's own life (vv 6-10: overconfidence leading to a sharp awareness of his weakness when God 'hid his face').

Exercise 5:   *Can you suggest what experience of life might have lain behind Psalm 30, when God hid his face 'and I was put to confusion' (v 7)?*

In Psalm 32:3-5 the singer relates another experience in his life; can you suggest what that experience was? In your own life, have you ever had the kind of experiences related in Psalms 30 and 32? Is this sharing of experiences what happens in a prayer meeting when someone gives a 'testimony'?

1.2   THE PSALMS AND LITURGY

Already it will be clear that the Psalms are not just private prayers for the use of individuals alone. They were used in the community, especially when the people gathered together for prayer.

As we have seen, in Psalms 30 and 116A the singer addresses both God and the people. In our study of the Psalms we need to take note of this: to whom is the psalmist speaking in a particular psalm? Indeed, who is in fact speaking — a single person, or the whole group, or a special section of the group? A few examples will show that psalms can differ widely in terms of who is being addressed and who is speaking:

Psalm 31:2

> In you, O Lord, I take refuge.
> Let me never be put to shame.
> In your justice, set me free,
> hear me and speedily rescue me

A prayer clearly addressed to God.

Psalm 62:8-9

> Take refuge in God all you people.
> Trust him at all times.
> Pour out your hearts before him
> for God is our refuge.

This is a teaching psalm addressed to the psalmist's companions, probably in the Temple. He draws on his own experience for his teaching.

Psalm 97

A hymn addressed partly to God ('For you indeed are the Lord most high above all the earth', *v 9*) and partly to the people ('Rejoice, you just, in the Lord; give glory to his holy name' *, 12*).

Psalm 101

A song sung by *one* person, in this case the King:

> *My* song is of mercy and justice,
> *I* sing to you, O Lord. (*v 1*)

Psalm 126

A song of the pilgrims on their way to Jerusalem:

> What marvels the Lord worked for us!
> Indeed we were glad.
> Deliver us, O Lord, from our bondage
> as streams in dry land. (*vv 3-4*)

Psalm 4 is an example, like Psalm 30, in which the singer addresses both God and the community:

1. When I call, answer me, O God of justice;
   from anguish you released me,
   have mercy and hear me!

   To God:
   a song of trust

2. O men, how long will your hearts be closed,
   will you love what is futile and seek what is false?

   To the community:
   a teaching

3. It is the Lord who grants favours to those
   whom he loves;
   the Lord hears me whenever I call him.

4. Fear him; do not sin: ponder on your bed
   and be still.

5. Make justice your sacrifice and trust in the Lord.

6. 'What can bring us happiness?' many say.
   Lift up the light of your face on us, O Lord.

   To God:
   continuing the song of trust

7. You have put into my heart a greater joy
   than they have from abundance of corn and new wine.

8. I will lie down in peace and sleep comes at once
   for you alone, Lord, make me dwell in safety.

Exercise 6: *Read Psalm 115 (113B in Grail). Who is being addressed in v 1, v 9, v 10 and v 11?*

Perhaps the best way to appreciate these changes in direction in some of the Psalms is to read *them aloud. Let someone in the group read aloud Psalms 4 and 30, so as to bring out who is being addressed in the different parts of these psalms. (Listening* to psalms and, *of course,* reading them aloud *are good ways to learn about them.)*

As we have seen, some of the Psalms involve a dialogue between the singer and the community; there are teachings and testimonies, and invitations to the community to join the psalmist in praising or thanking God. Likewise, there are psalms that were intended primarily for use in the Temple in Jerusalem; they were composed specifically for that purpose. For example, **Psalm 15** is part of an entrance ceremony at the Temple gate: the visitor or pilgrim wishes to enter this sacred place, and he asks:-

> Lord, who shall be admitted to your tent
> and dwell on your holy mountain?   *(v 1)*

A gatekeeper replies, describing the qualities needed to enter:

> He who walks without fault;
> he who acts with justice
> and speaks the truth from his heart;
> he who does not slander with his tongue;
> he who does no wrong to his brother,
> who casts no slur on his neighbour,
> who holds the godless in disdain,
> but honours those who fear the Lord;
> he who keeps his pledge, come what may;
> who takes no interest on a loan
> and accepts no bribes against the innocent.
> Such a man will stand firm for ever.   *(vv 2-5)*

Exercise 7: *Clearly very high standards of justice and kindness were expected of those who wished to enter the Temple. Read* Psalm 26; *do you think this would be a suitable reply to the Gatekeeper at the Temple in Psalm 15? And read Mark 11:15-17.*

Psalm 24 is another example of an entrance ceremony at the Temple gate:

Pilgrims:
1. The Lord's is the earth and its fullness,
   the world and all its peoples.   *Hymn of the pilgrims on*
                                              their way to the Temple
2. It is he who set it on the seas;
   on the waters he made it firm.

Leader:
3. Who shall climb the mountain of the Lord?   *Dialogue at the Temple gate*
   Who shall stand in his holy place?   *(see Psalm 15)*

Gatekeeper:
4. The man with clean hands and pure heart,
   who desires not worthless things,
   who has not sworn so as to deceive his neighbour.
5. He shall receive blessings from the Lord
   and reward from the God who saves him.

Leader:
6. Such are the men who seek him,
   seek the face of the God of Jacob.

Pilgrims:
7. O gates, lift high your heads;
   grow higher, ancient doors.
   Let him enter, the king of glory!

Temple Choir:
8. Who is the king of glory?
   The Lord, the mighty, the valiant,
   the Lord, the valiant in war.

Pilgrims:
9. O gates, lift high your heads;
   grow higher, ancient doors.
   Let him enter, the king of glory!

Temple Choir:
10. Who is he, the king of glory?
    He, the Lord of armies,
    he is the king of glory.

Choruses sung while entering the Temple

Psalm 24 preserves an elaborate entrance ceremony, from the hymn that the pilgrims sing as they make their way to the Temple, to the dialogue between the gatekeeper and the leader of the group, to what appears to be a choral exchange between the pilgrims and a Temple choir. (This last section, vv 7-10, may be a recalling of the time the Ark of the Covenant was carried into Jerusalem — see 2 Samuel 6:12-16). This kind of 'reconstruction' of the psalm is, of course, a matter of conjecture; in assigning different parts of the psalm to 'pilgrims', 'gatekeeper', 'Temple choir' etc., I am trying to show how Psalm 24 *may* have been sung (or perhaps better, *performed*) in the Temple. At this stage, no one can say with certainty exactly how the psalm was sung, but it is clear from the very form of the psalm itself that some kind of action was taking place through it.

The *liturgy* (i.e., the formal worship of the community in the Temple) was a drama: there were various roles to be played, there was movement, gesture, music, dialogue. The *body* played a part in the liturgy. The details of this worship are long since lost to us. Many of the Psalms belonged originally to Temple worship, but as we have them now they contain only the *script* for the liturgical drama. Few of the 'stage directions' remain, but it is sometimes possible, as with Psalm 24, to make an intelligent guess at what may have been happening 'behind' the psalm. Perhaps the best way to appreciate the psalms that are rooted in the liturgy of Israel is by *performing* them, by acting out how they may have originally been used in the Temple at Jerusalem.

Exercise 8:   *With some friends,* enact Psalm 24, *assigning parts to different people. Afterwards discuss in the group what you have learned from doing this.*

In studying these liturgical psalms it is important to be aware of such things as: Who is speaking? To whom? Is there only one person saying the psalm, or are there many speakers? Is there a dialogue going on? Does the psalm refer to objects, to particular people, to certain actions or activities?

Exercise 9:   *The following is part of a liturgical text: can you suggest from the text alone what may be happening?*

Blessed are you, Lord, God of all creation.
Through your goodness we have this bread to offer,
which earth has given and human hands have made.

9

It will become for us the bread of life.
Blessed be God forever.
By the mystery of this water and wine may we come to
share in the divinity of Christ, who humbled himself to
share in our humanity.
Blessed are you, Lord, God of all creation.
Through your goodness we have this wine to offer,
fruit of the vine and work of human hands.
It will become our spiritual drink.
Blessed be God forever.
Lord God, we ask you to receive us and be pleased with
the sacrifice we offer you with humble and contrite hearts.
Lord, wash away my iniquity; cleanse me from my sins.
Pray, brethren, that our sacrifice
may be acceptable to God, the almighty Father.
May the Lord accept the sacrifice at your hands
for the praise and glory of his name,
for our good, and the good of all his Church.

Many readers will recognise this passage at once: it is part of the Catholic Mass, and it refers to the preparation of the bread and wine. It is an interesting exercise to see how much information the text contains, and how much it reveals or suggests about what is taking place at that part of the Mass. Much the same is true of many of the Psalms: working from the text alone we can still discover a great deal about the background of the psalm and its original intention. For most of these 'liturgical psalms' the text is all that remains, but in some we can still find some instructions about their use — some of the 'stage directions' are still intact. For example:

Psalm 95:6
Come in; let us bow and bend low;
let us kneel before the God who made us.

Psalm 106:48
Blessed be the Lord, God of Israel,
for ever, from age to age.
Let all the people cry out:
'Amen! Amen! Alleluia!'

Compare this with the scene in Nehemiah 8:6 when Ezra is reading the Book of the Law to all the people — 'Then Ezra blessed Yahweh, the great God, and all the people raised their hands and answered, "Amen! Amen!"'; then they bowed down and, face to the ground, prostrated themselves before Yahweh.'

Psalm 118:27
Go forward in procession with branches
even to the altar.

And, of course, there are all the references to music-making and singing and marching and hand-clapping and dancing — these are not empty words!

Psalm 150:3-4
O praise him with sound of trumpet,
praise him with lute and harp.
Praise him with timbrel and dance,
praise him with strings and pipes.

Psalm 68:25-26
They see your solemn procession, O God,
the procession of my God, of my king, to the sanctuary:

the singers in the forefront, the musicians coming last,
between them, maidens sounding their timbrels.

It is clear that the worship of Israel was a lively, even a noisy, business. And if there were hymns to be sung, the title of the hymn would have to be announced to the congregation, as in *Psalm 124*:

Psalm 124   A song of salvation

Leader:

1. 'If the Lord had not been on our side,'
   this is Israel's song.

       Announcing the hymn

   All:

2. 'If the Lord had not been on our side
   when men rose against us,
3. then would they have swallowed us alive
   when their anger was kindled.
4. Then would the waters have engulfed us,
   the torrent gone over us;
5. over our head would have swept
   the raging waters.'

      The people sing the hymn,
an Exodus song recalling
their salvation through
the Red Sea waters.

Singer:

6. Blessed be the Lord who did not give us
   a prey to their teeth!
7. Our life, like a bird, has escaped
   from the snare of the fowler.
   Indeed the snare has been broken
   and we have escaped.
8. Our help is in the name of the Lord,
   who made heaven and earth.

      One singer or a choir
carries on the theme of the
Exodus song in other
images: escape from the
hunter and the bird-catcher
(see Psalm 91:3-4).
Hope in the NAME revealed
at the Exodus (Ex 3:13-15)

In the arrangement that I have suggested here, the leader announces the title of a well-known song — usually the first line of the song — and the congregation proceeds to sing it. Then a soloist, or the choir, continues the salvation theme of the hymn with new images — being saved from hunters and bird-catchers. The hymn title, 'If the Lord had not been on our side', may refer to the whole psalm, or perhaps only to verses 2-5 with their strong Exodus imagery.

Exercise 10:   *Read Psalm 124, assigning different parts to different people. Then go on to do the same thing with* Psalm 129 *which has a similar shape.*

Sometimes, as happens today, a psalm appears to have been written to the air of a well-known tune so that people can sing it easily. There are some psalms which still have in their titles the name of the appropriate tune. (These titles usually appear at the head of the psalm — as in *RSV, JB, NJB, NAB*. In the *Good News/TEV* translation they have been put in as footnotes to the psalm. Unfortunately, they are not reproduced at all in either the *Grail* or the *NEB* translations.)

Psalm 22   For the choirmaster   To 'The Doe of the Dawn'
Psalm 45   For the choirmaster   Tune: 'Lilies. . .'
Psalm 56   Tune: 'The oppression of distant princes'

Evidently, 'The Doe of the Dawn' and 'Lilies' and so on were popular songs at that time, which made it easier for the community to sing along with the choir.

All these 'stage directions', as they might be called, are not in themselves very important, yet they do remind us of the liturgical origins of many of the Psalms, and they can help us in our use of the Psalms today.

11

1.3 PROPHECY IN THE PSALMS

We have seen that entrance into the Temple was not something to be taken lightly or casually; it was felt that one must be in some way worthy to come into the presence of God in the holy place. And so, Psalms 15 and 24 describe entrance rituals at the Temple gates. Similarly, in *Psalm 95* a prophetic figure challenges those about to enter the Temple to be prepared to listen to God's word:

Psalm 95   A call to worship — a warning to heed the Word of God.

Leader:

1. Come, ring out our joy to the Lord;
   hail the rock who saves us.
2. Let us come before him, giving thanks,
   with songs let us hail the Lord.

Call to worship in the Temple

People:

3. A mighty God is the Lord,
   a great king above all gods.
4. In his hand are the depths of the earth;
   the heights of the mountains are his.
5. To him belongs the sea, for he made it
   and the dry land shaped by his hands.

Hymn as they go to the Temple, praising God the creator of all things

Leader:

6. Come in; let us bow and bend low;
   let us kneel before the God who made us
7. for he is our God and we
   the people who belong to his pasture,
   the flock that is led by his hand.

Instructions on how — and why — they are to worship God in the Temple

Prophet:

O that today you would listen to his voice!
8. Harden not your hearts as at Meribah,
   as on that day at Massah in the desert
9. when your fathers put me to the test;
   when they tried me, though they saw my work.
10. For forty years I was wearied of these people
    and I said: 'Their hearts are astray,
    these people do not know my ways.'
11. Then I took an oath in my anger:
    'Never shall they enter my rest.'

Prophecy spoken to the people at the Temple gate: Do not be deaf and stubborn like your ancestors!

In Psalm 95, the pilgrims are called to worship, and on the way they sing a typical hymn of praise to God who is Lord of heaven and earth. Then, at the entrance to the Temple, they are confronted by a prophet who challenges them with a message from God: they are about to enter his presence, his place of rest; well then, let them *listen* — something their ancestors in the desert did not do (read Exodus 17:1-7).

Exercise 11:   *Assign parts to different people and enact Psalm 95. Morning Prayer, as recited every day by priests, religious and many lay people in the Prayer of the Church, almost always begins with either Psalm 95 or Psalm 24. Why, do you think, were these psalms selected to begin the Church's daily prayer? Could they be adapted for use as penitential rites at the beginning of Mass or other religious services?*

I have described the guardian of the Temple gate in Psalm 95 as a *prophet*. Prophecy is not necessarily concerned with foretelling what is going to happen. Prophecy is a proclamation of the Word of God — the prophets always preface their statements with a phrase such as, 'Thus says the Lord', or 'The word of the Lord came to me saying. . .' The message is not the prophet's own; it is given to him, even though the style or idiom or actions may be shaped by the prophet himself, by his character and ability, by the circumstances, by the language used etc. Hence the great variety of language, stories, poetry, dramas, images and styles to be found in the works of such prophets as Hosea, Isaiah, Jeremiah, Ezekiel and so on.

It would seem that some psalms contain specific 'words of God' to be proclaimed on certain occasions. Entrance to the Temple appears to be a typical example: in addressing the people wishing to come into God's presence (as in Psalm 95:8-11), the gatekeeper is acting in a prophetic way. He is solemnly proclaiming God's word to the people on this occasion. There are other times, also preserved in the Psalms, when a word of prophecy is given to some Temple official to pronounce, as in *Psalm 85*:

Psalm 85

People:

1. O Lord, you once favoured your land
   and revived the fortunes of Jacob,
2. you forgave the guilt of your people
   and covered all their sins.
3. You averted all your rage,
   you calmed the heat of your anger.

4. Revive us now, God, our helper!
   Put an end to your grievance against us.
5. Will you be angry with us for ever,
   will your anger never cease?
6. Will you not restore again our life
   that your people may rejoice in you?
7. Let us see, O Lord, your mercy
   and give us your saving help.

A plea for help in a time of national danger

Prophet:

8. I will hear what the Lord God has to say:
   A voice that speaks of peace,
   peace for his people and his friends
   and those who turn to him in their hearts.
9. His help is near for those who fear him
   and his glory will dwell in our land.
10. Mercy and faithfulness have met;
    justice and peace have embraced.
11. Faithfulness shall spring from the earth
    and justice look down from heaven.

He speaks God's word of hope and peace.

Oracle

People:

12. The Lord will make us prosper
    and our earth shall yield its fruit.
13. Justice shall march before him
    and peace shall follow his steps.

Hymn of joy and hope arising from the word of the Lord

The whole psalm revolves around the oracle in verses 10-11, the reply of God to the prayers of his people. The people recognise it as a word of reassurance, and they respond with a hymn of joy and hope. Note how the words of the prophecy are introduced: 'I will hear what the Lord God has to say' (*v 8*). As always, the true prophet speaks not his own words, but God's

13

Word. In any psalm that contains a liturgical prophecy the relevant Word of God is always carefully indicated.

Exercise 12: *In the following psalms, can you suggest what would be the prophetic words? In each case note how the prophecy is introduced. Can you suggest the life-situation of each psalm?*

> Psalm 2
> Psalm 60
> Psalm 87
> Psalm 81
> Psalm 110

Today, when an appointed reader proclaims the Word of God at a Eucharist or some other liturgical service, he is acting in a prophetic way. He is given what he is to say by the Church (usually in the Lectionary or in the Ritual), he is appointed to this work, he proclaims to the Community. And so the readings always conclude, 'This is the Word of the Lord'. An understanding of the 'prophecy psalms' can help us to understand that the same prophetic event takes place at every liturgical celebration today — 'Oh, that today you would hear his voice!'

1.4 THE POETRY OF THE PSALMS

Poetry is not usually easy to translate from one language to another, but as it happens some of the best poetic features of the Hebrew psalsm can be reproduced in English. We will briefly look at two of these features: *imagery* and *parallelism*.

Imagery: The writers of the Psalms often used vivid, daring and memorable images to express their thoughts and prayers.

Psalm 56:8
No sorrow, no injustice goes unnoticed by God:

> Thou hast kept count of my tossings;
> put thou my tears in thy bottle!
> Are they not in thy book? (*RSV*)

Psalm 28:3-4
The voice of God can be heard in thunderclaps:

> The Lord's voice resounding on the waters;
> the voice of the Lord, full of power,
> the voice of the Lord, full of splendour. (*Grail*)

Psalm 102:7-8
The lonely sufferings of a man with many enemies:

> I have become like a pelican in the wilderness,
> like an owl in desolate places.
> I lie awake and I moan
> like some lonely bird on a roof. (*Grail*)

Exercise 13: *In the following lists the scripture references have, unfortunately, been mixed up; can you find the correct reference for each image described?*

> (1) A man of timber and caliber, solid as a cedar, who disappears into thin air   (A) Psalm 104:26
>
> (2) God plays with sea monsters   (B) Psalm 133:2

(3)	Dancing mountains	(C)	Psalm 37:35-36
(4)	Important men — heavyweights who rise *when put in a scales*	(D)	Psalm 22:13-14,17
(5)	Ointment flowing over a person's hair and face	(E)	Psalm 62:10
(6)	The sea is like a wrapper, the sky like a tarpaulin	(F)	Psalm 114:4
(7)	My enemies are bulls, lions, dogs	(G)	Psalm 104:3-6

Parallelism: This is a very simple way of adding to the delight and depth of meaning of a psalm: the writer combines two or three lines in such a way that the later lines carry on the thought of the first one, either to repeat it, add to it, or respond to it.

Psalm 18:7
In my anguish I called to the Lord;
I cried to my God for help.

Psalm 26:5
I hate the evil-doer's company:
I will not take my place with the wicked.

In each case, the second line simply repeats the sense of the first line, expressing it in another way.

Psalm 18:20
He brought me forth into freedom,
he saved me because he loved me.

Here the second line repeats the thought of the first, and adds a new idea — he was saved *because of the love of God.*

Psalm 100   is a call to prayer, to enter the Temple and praise God the Faithful Creator. The psalm is made up of four verses of three lines each; the sequence of lines in each verse strengthens and develops the thought of that verse.

1. Cry out with joy to the Lord, all the earth.   *Praise the Lord,*
2. Serve the Lord with gladness.
   Come before him, singing for joy.

3. Know that he, the Lord, is God.   *for he is our God;*
   He made us, we belong to him,
   we are his people, the sheep of his flock.

4. Go within his gates, giving thanks.   *Thank him in the Temple.*
   Enter his courts with songs of praise.
   Give thanks to him and bless his name.

5. Indeed, how good is the Lord,   *for God is good.*
   eternal his merciful love.
   He is faithful from age to age.

In the examples we have seen, the sequence of lines put in parallel tends to reinforce the initial statement, either by repeating it in other words, or by adding a new element. There is another way that parallelism can be used — to set up a contrast between one line and another:

Psalm 37:21-22
The wicked man borrows and cannot repay,
but the just man is generous and gives.
Those blessed by the Lord shall own the land,
but those he has cursed shall be destroyed.

15

Luke 1:52-53
He casts the mighty from their thrones
and raises the lowly.
He fills the starving with good things
and sends the rich away empty.

Psalm 57:7
They laid a snare for my steps,
my soul was bowed down.
They dug a pit in my path
but fell in it themselves.

In this last example, the psalmist has built up a sequence of lines describing how his enemies were working against him — the final line turns the whole scheme around, and his enemies are caught in their own trap!

Parallelism is a very common feature of Hebrew poetry, and it adds to the beauty of the psalms. But it can also be a way of exploring new ideas and of searching for new meanings. By placing statements and ideas in parallel, the psalmist sets up a kind of dialogue between them: the second line can add a new dimension to the first. For example, *Psalm 51* is a powerful prayer of repentance arising out of a deep awareness of sinfulness — the psalmist asks that in God's great compassion he might be washed from his guilt and cleansed from his sin (*vv 3 and 4*). However, this is no mere external washing but an inner re-creation:

12. A pure heart create for me, O God,
    put a steadfast spirit within me.
13. Do not cast me away from your presence,
    nor deprive me of your holy spirit.
14. Give me again the joy of your help;
    with a spirit of fervour sustain me.

Exercise 14:   *What is the psalmist saying in these verses? Examine the use of parallelism here, and see how in each verse the second line enlarges the meaning of the first line. The psalmist links the three verses with the word 'spirit' — what does this tell us about the spirit and forgiveness?*

Another example of parallelism being used to explore God's ways with us concerns the *justice* of God, for justice in the Bible may not be exactly the same as *our* idea of it. *Psalm 36* sets up a parallel between love and justice:

11. Keep on loving those who know you,
    doing justice for upright hearts.
12. Let the foot of the proud not crush me
    nor the hand of the wicked cast me out.

The same connection is made in *Psalm 143*:

11. For your name's sake, Lord, save my life;
    in your justice save my soul from distress.
12. In your love make an end of my foes,
    destroy all those who oppress me
    for I am your servant, O Lord.

It would seem that, for the psalmist at least, God's justice is mainly concerned with helping those who are in need, rescuing those who are oppressed, forgiving those who have sinned. His 'justice' and his 'love' are much closer than we might imagine, and by placing them in parallel the psalmist opens up new possibilities in understanding God.

Exercise 15:   *Psalm 31:2-3 says:*

> *In your justice, set me free,*
> *hear me and speedily rescue me.*

Weekday Preface II *in the Catholic Missal says:*

> *In love you created man,*
> *in justice you condemned him,*
> *but in mercy you redeemed him. . .*

Do you think the word 'justice' has the same meaning in each example? What is your understanding of justice?

1.5 A BOOK OF PRAISES

As we have seen, some of the Psalms were composed by individual poets out of their own life experiences — psalms of need, of sorrow, of joy, of sharing with the rest of the community. Other psalms seem to have been written specifically for the formal worship of Israel in the Temple in Jerusalem — psalms of entry to the Temple, psalms containing prophecies, psalms of praise to be accompanied by music and dancing. And as we shall see in this course, there are other kinds of psalms too — songs of the Story of Israel, laments over national disasters, celebrations for the King and his armies, hymns of hope for the future of God's people. There were many sources that contributed to the collection we now have in the Psalter.

One clue to the way in which the Psalter was formed can be found in the names that are attached to some psalms:

> Psalm 83 'of Asaph'
> Psalm 84 'of the sons of Korah'

The individuals named, Asaph and Korah, were probably composers or well-known choirmasters whose work proved so popular that it became part of the general collection. The 'sons of Korah' were possibly his students, who would have preserved and handed on his work. These 'named' psalms sometimes fall into small groups, which may originally have been local collections or hymn-books only later gathered into the Psalter; for example, Psalms 73-83 are all 'of Asaph'.

Exercise 16:   *There are other psalms 'of Asaph' and 'of the sons of Korah'; please list them.*
What groupings do you notice?

Other names are found at the head of some psalms, among them some well-known personages — Moses, David, Solomon. In fact a great number of psalms are attributed to David, including two major groupings, Psalms 3-41 and Psalms 51-70. It is not certain that any of these psalms was, in fact, composed by David (or by Moses or Solomon). However, David was known to have been a 'skilled harpist' (see 1 Samuel 16:14-23) and traditionally was given credit for much of Israel's song and music. So it is not surprising that some psalms were not only ascribed to him, but were given titles that suggested they belonged to certain incidents in David's life.

Psalm 3
'When he was fleeing from his son Absalom'
(see 2 Samuel 15:1-23)

Psalm 57
'When he escaped from Saul in the cave'
(see 1 Samuel 24:1-23)

Psalm 63

'When he was in the desert of Judah'
(see 1 Samuel 23:14)
In his longing for God, whose Temple is so far away, the soul of the singer is like the desert around him, 'a dry, weary land without water'.

We should remember that these psalms were almost certainly not written by David himself, still less on the occasions suggested in the headings. What we have here is a continuation and at the same time almost the reverse of the process we have seen already in which a life-situation gives rise to a psalm. In the case of Psalms 3, 57 and 63 (and others like them), the experience of an anonymous singer produced a psalm which was later fitted into the context of an incident in the life of David. Two things are happening here: the psalm is retaining its connection with life, and at the same time it is taking on a more universal application — it is being made available to all of us.

Exercise 17: *Read* 2 Samuel 11:1-12:15, *and then* Psalm 51 *which has the following heading:*

For the choirmaster: Psalm of David. When the prophet Nathan had come to him because he had gone to Bathsheba

Does the psalm fit this incident in the life of David? When would we say this psalm?

All this was part of the process whereby these scattered songs and groups of songs were gathered into the great collection of the Psalter. There they were joined by hymns written in the Temple itself, possibly by professional composers writing for specific liturgical events. All together, they formed a kind of Temple Hymnbook. Towards the end of the gathering process, the collection was divided into *five groups*, each group ending with a special verse in praise of God.

1) Psalms 1-41
Blessed be the Lord, the God of Israel
from age to age. Amen. Amen.   *(41:13)*

2) Psalms 42-72
Blessed be the Lord, God of Israel,
who alone works wonders,
ever blessed his glorious name.
Let his glory fill the earth.
Amen! Amen!   *(72:19)*

3) Psalms 73-89
Blessed be the Lord for ever.
Amen, Amen!   *(89:52)*

4) Psalms 90-106
Blessed be the Lord, God of Israel,
for ever, from age to age.
Let all the people cry out:
'Amen! Amen! Alleluia!'   *(106:48)*

5) Psalms 107-150
See Psalm 150: the entire psalm is a hymn of praise which concludes not just the fifth group, but the whole Book of Psalms.

This division into five groups was possibly intended to imitate the five-fold character of the first part of the Hebrew Bible, the so-called *Pentateuch* — *Genesis, Exodus, Leviticus, Numbers* and *Deuteronomy*. These are the books ascribed to Moses, and known in the tradition of the Jewish people as the *Torah* or Law.

In this first chapter we have been mainly concerned with the origins and formation of the Psalter. In the history of the Psalter and its use we can detect two movements. The first was a *tendency towards the Temple*. The psalms that arose out of the life-situations of individuals or events in the history of the people were preserved, gathered in small collections, and eventually found their way into the larger Temple collections. There they met with psalms that were specifically part of Temple liturgy, and — sometime before 400 BC — were assembled into the collection as we have it now. This book became part of the resources of the Temple in celebrating the worship of Israel. A final step was taken when this same collection was included in the third section of the Hebrew Bible, 'the *Writings*', thus giving it the same scriptural status as the *Law* and the *Prophets* (see Luke 24:44 where Jesus refers to 'everything written about me in the Law of Moses, in the Prophets and in the Psalms'). The Psalms, too, are the word of God!

This process of bringing psalms to the Temple, the central place of worship for the Jewish people, was matched by a *movement in the opposite direction*. As the Jewish people spread over the known world (especially after the Babylonian Captivity in the sixth century BC) it was no longer possible for them to take part in the worship of a central Temple in Jerusalem. There were no other temples, so the focus of community prayer changed to the *Synagogue*, a meeting place in each community of Jews where the Scriptures were listened to and discussed, and where the people could join in praising God through the psalms and other hymns. The Synagogue was of vast importance in making the Sacred Scriptures known to the community in general, particularly at a time when written works (books or scrolls) were extremely rare, and when the majority of the people were illiterate. In order to join in common prayer in the synagogue or the Temple, they had to learn psalms by heart, or at least parts of them — responses and refrains, for instance. These remembered lines and poems would then have become a resource for individual and private prayer too. In a sense, the Psalms had come back to the people again.

1.6 THE PSALMS AND PRAYER

The Psalms are prayers: to be properly understood they need to be prayed. The aim of this course is, in the end, to help us in praying the Psalms. Prayer should go hand-in-hand with our study. So, even though it means mentioning some aspects that we have not yet studied, I would like to make some brief comments at this stage on prayer in the Psalms.

The Psalms and the prayer of the Hebrews

a) Notice how their prayer is rooted in life and experience: the troubles and joys of life; their history and liturgy; danger and rescue; sickness, infancy and old age; exile and pilgrimage; loneliness and friendship. . . Note all the bodily references: hands, feet, throat, skin, head, eyes — all subject to abuse and suffering, all used in gestures of prayer. In brief, the psalmist is aware of God and meets God in his own life and place and body, and in the life and company of his own people.

b) The *honesty* of the psalmist. If he is happy he says so; if angry or fearful he says so. If he is angry with *God*, he says that too (Psalms 44 and 74). The psalmist is in touch with his own feelings and emotions, and this helps him to appreciate the feelings and emotions of God — *his* anger and pity and longing. The Psalms can be very violent in God's cause — the enemies of God must be destroyed, and the psalmist is quite willing to do that work for God (Psalms 83 and 139). The so-called 'cursing psalms' arise out of this simplicity and honesty: my enemies are God's enemies, so they do not deserve to live! The psalmist's passionate love for Jerusalem is matched by an equally ardent hatred for Jerusalem's destroyers (Psalm 137). Even though it sometimes leads to what we would call 'unChristian attitudes', at least there is a certain honesty and truth about the psalmist's prayers; he does not pretend to be better than he is. (Today the cursing elements in the Psalms clash with the command of Christ that we are to love even our enemies. But there is no reason for us to feel superior to the ancient Hebrews and their morality; Christians have a very poor record in the matter of dealing with their enemies. Whatever about our prayers, there is a certain lack of mercy in our history.)

c) *God is the centre of the prayer* of the Psalms. The psalmist is very aware of himself, but is even more intensely aware of what God has done and is doing. God is utterly transcendant (beyond our reach), and yet he is intimately involved with us (Psalm 139). No problem is too big or too small — the timid fears of a frail old person (Psalm 71) or the danger posed by the powerful nations that threaten to crush Israel (Psalm 2). God is delightful, loving, mysterious, terrifying, and dangerous.

d) The *liturgy*, the worship of the people gathered in community, is a privileged place and time for praying the Psalms. The 'great assembly' is the ideal setting for praising God. And so, many psalms have been created or adapted for liturgical use. Even when prayed in solitude there is in the Psalms a constant awareness of the rest of the community with whom life, salvation and prayer are shared. And the mind of the psalmist is ever broadened out from the narrow confines of his own individual experience: others rejoice and grieve with him, he is not alone.

The Psalms and Christian prayer

e) All the remarks made above about Hebrew prayer apply here too. The one who sings the Psalms today is of the same human stock as the Hebrew psalmist. It is perhaps our common humanity that makes us recognise so quickly the suitability of the Psalms for our prayer, despite the many differences in culture, religion, morality and language. Prayer today needs to be rooted in our lives, to be honest and true, to be centred on God the Father of Jesus Christ. And the 'great assembly' is found in our churches too.

f) What may be most important is not what the psalms say *for* us in prayer, but what they say *to* us. In a sense, more than any other part of the Scriptures, the psalms are the Word of God in human words. God's love and compassion are discovered through the human experience of life, and in the way that experience is gathered into prayer. We need to *listen to the Psalms*. To listen is to pray, to acknowledge the Divine Voice behind the Psalms. (That is why there is a special value in listening to a psalm being read by another person, or if you are alone, in reading a psalm *aloud*).

g) As we shall see throughout this course, Christ has 'fulfilled' the Psalms (see Luke 24:44). They find their most complete expression and meaning in Jesus' life and on his lips; they are how he speaks with his beloved Father. Today Christians pray the Psalms as members of the Body of Christ; they unite their praying with that of the beloved Son. This is above all true when the psalms are prayed in the liturgy of the Church.

Exercise 18:   *More a suggestion than an exercise: for us too it can be helpful to* learn by heart *some favourite psalms or verses. Particularly for certain attitudes of prayer — sorrow for sin, thankfulness, joy, desire for God, trust, etc. — such remembered psalms would be available for prayer at any time, in any place.*

2 THE STORY

In this chapter we turn to the history of the People of Israel, and what it tells us about them and about God. What is the significance of their story and how they told it? And what of *our* history — what story have *we* to tell?

2.1 A QUESTION OF IDENTITY

At any time people are interested in their own history, in the stories of their past and of the men and women who were their ancestors, in the tales of the things that happened to them and of how they began as a people, and in the legends of long ago. We want to know our roots. If we know these things, then we have a better idea of who we are, what our identity is. The people of Israel were no different: they too wanted to know themselves, their history, their identity. The Book of *Deuteronomy* envisages a situation in which just such questions were asked:

> In times to come, when your child asks you, 'What is the meaning of these instructions, laws and customs which Yahweh our God has laid down for you'. . .
>
> > (In other words, 'What is the meaning of our lives and the things that we do? Who are we? Where have we come from?')
> >
> > . . . you are to tell your child, 'Once we were Pharaoh's slaves in Egypt, and Yahweh brought us out of Egypt by his mighty hand. Before our eyes, Yahweh worked great and terrible signs and wonders against Egypt, against Pharaoh and his entire household. And he brought us out of there, to lead us into the country which he had sworn to our ancestors that he would give us. And Yahweh has commanded us to observe all these laws and to fear Yahweh our God, so as to be happy for ever and to survive, as we do to this day. For us, right living will mean this: to keep and observe all these commandments in obedience to Yahweh our God, as he has commanded us'. (*6:20-25*)

This then is the story, or at least part of the story, that tells how the People came to be, and how they came to be in the land of Canaan. The fuller outline of the story can be found in the books of the Bible that run from *Genesis* to *Joshua*.

Exercise 19:   *The following selection of texts from various books of the Bible outline the story from the call of Abraham to the entry into the Promised Land. Please read them, and for each text write out the main points of that part of the story in the space provided.*

Genesis 12:1-8; 15:1-21	Call of **Abraham**; promise of descendants who will one day occupy the land of the Canaanites. Another version of this call, and a *covenant* with Abraham.
Genesis 18:1-15; 21:1-7	
Genesis 25:19-28	
Genesis 46:1-7	
Exodus 1:1-22	
Exodus 2:23-3:20; 6:2-13	
Exodus 11:1-10; 12:29-32	
Exodus 13:17-14:31	
Exodus 16:1-15	
Exodus 19:1-20:21; 25	
Joshua 1:1-9; 3:1-4:18	God gives the Land of Canaan to the People, and under the leadership of Joshua they cross the Jordan and enter the Land.

Now that you have read this part of the story of Israel, tell in your own words, or discuss in groups: What did God do for his people?

By telling their story, by recalling the events of their past, the people established their own identity. Perhaps we can understand this a little better by doing the same thing for ourselves, by telling our own story.

Exercise 20: *What is your story? Who are you? Either as an individual or as a group, try to tell your own story. Here are two possible ways of doing this:*

(1) On a sheet of paper, trace a line beginning with your birth and passing through the important events, people and places of your life. You could mark times of special joy or difficulty, even making small drawings to illustrate these. In groups of three or four, share as much as you wish of your story, and listen to the others' stories. (It is important to just listen — this is an experience in trust, in receiving a gift from someone else. Don't judge or criticise.) What do you learn from doing this exercise? Does your story have anything in common with the stories of your friends?

(2) For a group: Put a large strip of newsprint or paper on a wall, and mark it off into sections corresponding to ten-year periods:

1937 — 1946	1947 — 1956	1957 — 1966	1967 — 1976	1977 — 1986	1987

Beginning with the current year (say, 1987) and working back *through the decades, let the group mark down the more significant facts, events, attitudes, people etc. in the story of* this community. *How far back does the 'group memory' go? How does the story of this group or community correspond with the wider stories of the nation or the Church?*

Do you think such exercises as these can help us to understand ourselves better, and to know more about who we are?

2.2 SONG AND STORY

The memory of a people is filled with stories and songs and traditions that are passed on from generation to generation:

Give heed, my people, to my teaching,
turn your ear to the words of my mouth.
I will open my mouth in a parable
and reveal hidden lessons of the past.
The things we have heard and understood,
the things our fathers have told us
these we will not hide from their children
but will tell them to the next generation:
the glories of the Lord and his might
and the marvellous deeds he has done. . .   *Ps 78:1-7*

It was these 'glories of the Lord' and his 'marvellous deeds' that made the people what they are now. The story we have seen outlined in the books of *Genesis, Exodus* and *Joshua* (see Exercise 19) becomes the basis for songs of praise.

Psalm 105
vv   1-6   A call to praise
vv   7-11   The covenant God made with Abraham and his descendants
vv 12-45   The Story: how God kept his promise

A hymn of praise telling the story from the beginning: 'the covenant he made with *Abraham*, the oath he swore to *Isaac*. He confirmed it for *Jacob* as a law, for Israel as a covenant for ever' (*vv 9-10*). 'Israel' is another name for Jacob (see Genesis 32:27-28; 35:10); the 'people of Israel' meaning the people descended from Israel/Jacob. The promise made by God: 'I am giving you a land, Canaan, your appointed heritage' (*v 11*). The rest of the psalm recalls how *Joseph* came to Egypt, the sufferings of his people there, their release by the power of God and his granting them 'the land of the nations', i.e. Canaan. The promise has been fulfilled and the singers of this song are now in the very Land of Promise, so that 'they might keep his precepts, that thus they might observe his laws' (*v 45*. See also Deuteronomy 6:23-25, where living in the Land also means keeping God's law.)

Psalm 78
The same story, with a stress on the events at the Red Sea ('He divided the sea and led them through and made the waters stand up like a wall.' *v 13*) and on the persistent ingratitude of the people ('For their hearts were not truly with him; they were not faithful to his covenant' *v 37*). The events referred to in this psalm can also be found in *Exodus 12-17, Numbers 11* and *Deuteronomy 32*. The uncaring attitude of the people contrasts with the constant mercy of God: 'he who is full of compassion forgave their sin and spared them' *v 38*. The story of this

enduring love of God is continued down to the time of David whom God called 'to be shepherd of Jacob his people, of Israel his own possession' (*v 71*).

Psalm 135

Yet another answer to the question, 'Who are we?' We are God's own people. He is 'our God' not because we own him (as if he were a dead idol, *vv 15-18*) but because *he* owns *us* — 'For the Lord has chosen Jacob for himself and Israel for his own possession' (*v 4*). This psalm celebrates a *living God*, who has done great deeds and is now to be praised for his goodness and love (*v 3*). This psalm has its roots in the Temple worship of Israel — those called upon to praise God are the 'servants of the Lord, who stand in the house of the Lord' (*v 2*), as well as special groupings, the Sons of Israel, Sons of Aaron, Sons of Levi, and those who fear the Lord (see Psalms 115 and 118 for similar groupings). So this Temple-song recalls the story of God's saving deeds, and ends with a home-coming for the Lord himself: 'From Zion may the Lord be blessed, *he who dwells in Jerusalem!*' (*v 21*).

All these psalms tell the story of Israel — and we must never forget it:

When Yahweh has brought you into the country which he swore to your ancestors Abraham, Isaac and Jacob that he would give you, with great and prosperous cities you have not built, with houses full of good things you have not provided, with wells you have not dug, with vineyards and olive trees you have not planted, and then, when you have eaten as much as you want, be careful you do not forget Yahweh who has brought you out of Egypt, out of the place of slave-labour.   *Dt 6:10-12*

To forget God and what he did for them would be to forget themselves. Every step they took on the land was a reminder to them of who they were and how they had come to be (see Joshua 1:3). Their identity was to be found not only in their history, but in their geography too.

Exercise 21: *The map on page 25 shows the World of the Psalms, through which the people of Israel travelled in the Exodus, and in which they and their neighbours lived. Can you find on the map the places mentioned in the psalms, such as:-*

Egypt	Edom	Canaan	Jerusalem
Bashan	Red Sea	River Nile	River Jordan
Dead Sea	Sinai		

2.3 WHO IS GOD? ANOTHER QUESTION OF IDENTITY

The people of Israel saw God in their history, and in their geography. Their story not only identifies them; it identifies God too. He is the beginning of their story, from the time he called Abraham and Sarah down to this day. He is the God who made the first move, the God who calls, the faithful God. But above all, *the God who listens*: 'Yahweh then said, ''I have indeed seen the misery of my people in Egypt. I have heard them crying for help. . .'' ' (*Ex 3:7*). This cry of the oppressed people in Egypt is but one of a long series of cries that have come to God's hearing, from the murder of Abel whose 'blood is crying out to me from the ground' (*Gn 4:10*), to the 'outcry against Sodom and Gomorrah' (*Gn 18:20*), to the anguish of the one who shouted, 'out of the depths I cry to you, O Lord' (*Ps 130:1*), to the crying out of 'the wages which you kept back from the labourers mowing your fields' (*Jm 5:4*), and, in the end, to Calvary: 'Jesus cried out in a loud voice. . . ''My God, my God, why have you forsaken me?'' ' (*Mt 27:46*).

In the experience of the people of Israel, God is a 'God of tenderness and compassion, slow to anger, rich in faithful love and constancy.' (*Ex 34:6*). The story of Israel is founded on precisely

24

this 'faithful love and constancy'. 'Yahweh set his heart on you and chose you not because you were the most numerous of all people — for indeed you were the smallest of all — but because he loved you and meant to keep the oath which he swore to your ancestors: that was why Yahweh brought you out with his mighty hand and redeemed you from the place of slave-labour, from the power of Pharaoh king of Egypt' (*Ex 7:7-8*).

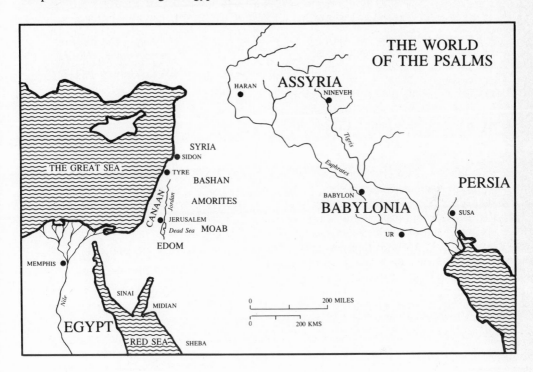

The Exodus from Egypt revealed God to us: 'I am the LORD your God who brought you out of the land of Egypt, out of the house of bondage. You shall have no other gods before me' (*Ex 20:2-3* — the opening lines of the ten commandments). This is the beginning of the realisation that there is only one God — the one who hears the cry of the oppressed. And yet, it is so easy to forget God, as *Psalm 81* shows: this is a psalm calling the people to celebrate at a Harvest festival. The psalm contains a prophecy (see section 1.3 of these notes) built around a proclamation of the first commandment in Exodus 20:2-3.

Psalm 81

Leader:

2. Ring out your joy to God our strength,
   shout in triumph to the God of Jacob.
3. Raise a song and sound the timbrel,
   the sweet-sounding harp and the lute,
4. blow the trumpet at the new moon,
   when the moon is full, on our feast.
5. For this is Israel's law,
   a command of the God of Jacob.
6. He imposed it as a rule on Joseph,
   when he went out against the land of Egypt.

Call to worship, possibly at the feast of Tabernacles — a harvest festival.

Prophet:

A voice I did not know said to me:	Prophecy: *Remember that*
7. 'I freed your shoulder from the burden;	*they are a redeemed people,*
your hands were freed from the load.	*set free from slavery, tested*
8. You called in distress and I saved you.	*in the desert (see Psalm*
I answered, concealed in the storm cloud,	*95:7)*
at the waters of Meribah I tested you.	
9. Listen, my people, to my warning,	*A reminder of the first*
O Israel, if only you would heed!	*commandment (Exodus*
10. Let there be no foreign god among you,	*20:2-3) and of who God is*
no worship of an alien god.	
11. I am the Lord your God,	
who brought you from the land of Egypt.	
Open wide your mouth and I will fill it.	
12. But my people did not heed my voice	*The disobedience of the*
and Israel would not obey,	*people at the time of the*
13. so I left them in their stubborness of heart	*Exodus; what of the people*
to follow their own designs.	*of today? (see Psalm*
14. O that my people would heed me,	*95:8-11)*
that Israel would walk in my ways!	
15. At once I would subdue their foes,	
turn my hand against their enemies.	
16. The Lord's enemies would cringe at their feet	
and their subjection would last for ever.	
But Israel I would feed with finest wheat	*The harvest: a sign of*
and fill them with honey from the rock.'	*God's love and fidelity*

Note the similarities between Psalm 81 and Psalm 95 (see p.12).

Exercise 22:   *Enact Psalm 81. Note how vv 10-11 recall the first commandment (reversing the order of Exodus 20:2-3 by putting the warning about alien gods before the proclamation, 'I am the Lord your God. . .'). So the commandment becomes part of the prophetic warning to the people — once again, a prophet speaks not his own words but God's word.*

Can you suggest the importance of this commandment to our lives today?

2.4 THE PATTERN OF HIS PITY

The real significance of Israel's story was not that it related an accurate history of events but that it was a way of seeing things, a way of seeing themselves, a way of seeing God. And one of the things seen through the story was a *pattern* — the pattern of God's pity. God's love sharpened his ear to hear the cry of his oppressed people, and he led them to freedom with mighty hand and outstretched arm. And he established a pattern, a way of acting typical of him, so that to his people — to all oppressed people — *he gave a right to be heard.*

Psalm 107
The pattern of God's pity is perhaps best reflected in this psalm, yet another variation on the theme of the *hesed* of God: 'O give thanks to the Lord for he is good; for his love endures for ever' (*v 1*). Four situations of need are described, to each of which God responds: he hears their cry, and sets them free.

4. Some wandered in the desert, in the wilderness,
   finding no way to a city they could dwell in.
5. Hungry they were and thirsty;
   their soul was fainting within them.

The need: lost and hungry
people

6a. Then they cried to the Lord in their need

The cry!

6b. and he rescued them from their distress
7. and he led them along the right way,
   to reach a city they could dwell in.

God hears and acts

8. Let them thank the Lord for his love,
   for the wonders he does for men.
9. For he satisfies the thirsty soul;
   he fills the hungry with good things.

Song of thanksgiving

Exercise 23: *The pattern of vv 4-9 shown above is repeated for three other situations of need in Psalm 107. What are those needs and how does God respond to them? For your answer, fill in the verse numbers and descriptions in the followng grid:*

vv 10-16	vv 17-22	vv 23-32	The pattern
			The need
			The cry
			God hears and acts
			Song of thanksgiving

Can you suggest present-day examples of the needs described in Psalm 107? What general conclusions does the psalmist draw from God's attitudes and way of acting (vv 33-44)?

Psalm 143

The prayer of someone oppressed by her enemy who 'has crushed my life to the ground; he has made me dwell in darkness' (v 3). In her desperate need she remembers God's deeds in 'the days that are past: I ponder all your works' (v 5). In the confidence of that memory she cries out: 'Rescue me, Lord, from my enemies: I have fled to you for refuge' (v 9). Where else would she flee? The pattern of God's pity is seen in this song, as it is in many of the psalms of individual suffering that we have already seen (for example, Psalms 4 and 30).

Psalm 83

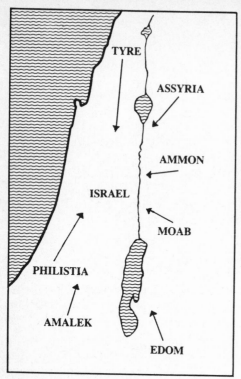

The story of the Exodus from Egypt and the constant faithfulness of God becomes the basis for hope whenever the people are threatened. *Psalm 83* is a call to God to destroy the enemies of Israel. The psalmist imagines the country surrounded by *all* her traditional foes: Edom, Moab, Ammon, Tyre, the Assyrians, Amalekites, Philistines etc. He is, in fact, exaggerating; though each of these was, at one time or another, at war with Israel, there was never a time when they all banded together against her. Still, the psalmist calls on God to help Israel in her present crisis — whatever it was. He wants God to act for her as he had done in the time of the Judges (note how vv 10-13 refer to Judges 4-8). He prays that the pattern of God's pity would be seen for his people *now*.

All Israel's enemies make 'common alliance' against her (v6).

Psalm 80 *is a lament for the community, and may have been prayed like this:*

Choir:

2. O shepherd of Israel, hear us,
   you who lead Joseph's flock,
   shine forth from your cherubim throne
3. upon Ephraim, Benjamin, Manasseh.
   O Lord, rouse up your might,
   O Lord, come to our help.

INVOCATION *using traditional imagery of the Shepherd and his flock (see Psalms 23; 100; Isaiah 40:11). Three Northern tribes are named (v 3) — a time of danger for the North?*

All:

4. God of Hosts, bring us back;
   let your face shine on us and we shall be saved.

RESPONSE, *see Numbers 6:24-26*

Choir:

5. Lord God of Hosts, how long
   will you frown on your people's plea?
6. You have fed them with tears for their bread,
   an abundance of tears for their drink.
7. You have made us the taunt of our neighbours,
   our enemies laugh us to scorn.

LAMENT *in a time of national danger: is all this God's own doing?*

All:

8. God of hosts, bring us back;
   let your face shine on us and we shall be saved.

RESPONSE

Leader:

9. You brought a vine out of Egypt;
   to plant it you drove out the nations.
10. Before it you cleared the ground;
    it took root and spread through the land.
11. The mountains were covered with its shadow,
    the cedars of God with its boughs.
12. It stretched out its branches to the sea,
    to the Great River it stretched out its shoots.
13. Then why have you broken down its walls?
    It is plucked by all who pass by.
14. It is ravaged by the boar of the forest,
    devoured by the beasts of the field.

THE STORY: *parable of the Vine (see Genesis 49:22; Isaiah 5:1-7; Hosea 10:1)*

All:

15. God of hosts, turn again, we implore,
    look down from heaven and see.

RESPONSE

Choir:

16. Visit this vine and protect it,
    the vine your right hand has planted.
17. Men have burned it with fire and destroyed it.
    May they perish at the frown of your face.
18. May your hand be on the man you have chosen,
    the man you have given your strength.
19. And we shall never forsake you again:
    give us life that we may call upon your name.

SUPPLICATION *Inspired by the parable of the vine*

All:

20. God of hosts, bring us back;
    let your face shine on us and we shall be saved.

RESPONSE

The Parable of the Vine (Psalm 80: 9-14, 16-17). In reminding God of his great saving deeds in the past, the psalmist draws on two of the best-known images in biblical language: the *shepherd and his flock* and the *vine*. Among the prophets the image of the vine or vineyard for Israel was a favourite. In most cases the significance was the same: the vine runs wild and produces poor fruit despite the best care of God the gardener (see Isaiah 5:1-7; 27:3-5; Ezekiel 17:3-10; 19:10-14). Jesus continued the metaphor in the story of the vineyard rented to untrustworthy tenants (Matthew 21:33-44) and especially in the daring identification of himself with the 'true vine' (see John 15:1-17) — a vine which will indeed bear much fruit, but which will also be 'ravaged by the boar of the forest, devoured by the beasts of the field' (*Ps 80:14*).

The complaint of Psalm 80 is that God has left his vineyard unprotected (vv 13-14). Whereas it had flourished under his former care (vv 9-12), stretching from the Mediterranean Sea to the Euphrates river (a reminder of the extent of the kingdom in Solomon's time), now it is at the mercy of all predators. Hence the repeated cry that the 'God of Hosts' would intervene, 'bring us back' (vv 4, 8, 20) and, in the key verse of the psalm (a variation of the response) 'turn again . . . look down from heaven and see' (v 15). They have felt the absence of God, they finally admit that it is *they who have left God*, and they promise that they will never forsake him again (v 19).

Exercise 24:   *Enact Psalm 80. You will notice that this is one of those psalms with a musical direction — 'For the Choirmaster   Tune: "The decrees are lilies"' (see Chapter 1.2, page 6). Perhaps some musical member of the group could compose a suitable tune, at least for the response!*

After you have enacted the psalm, discuss in small groups whether this psalm relates to any experience in your life.

2.5 THE NAME OF GOD

The story of Israel identifies God; it also gives us his name:

> Moses then said to God, 'Look, if I go to the Israelites and say to them, "The God of your ancestors has sent me to you", and they say to me, "What is his name?" "What am I to tell them?" God said to Moses, 'I am he who is.' And he said, 'This is what you are to say to the Israelites, "I am has sent me to you". God further said to Moses, 'You are to tell the Israelites, "Yahweh, the God of your ancestors, the God of Abaham, the God of Isaac and the God of Jacob, has sent me to you". This is my name for all time, and thus I am to be invoked for all generations to come.' *(Ex 3:13-15)*

This reply of God both conceals and reveals him. 'I am he who is' (in a shorter form, 'I am' in v 14) assures us of God's presence, but what that presence means is revealed only in the story of what he has done. That the God of the burning bush *belongs* to the story is evident from v 15 — he is 'Yahweh, the God of your ancestors', Abraham, Isaac, Jacob. Another account of the meeting between Moses and God makes the matter even clearer: 'God spoke to Moses and said to him, "I am Yahweh. To Abraham, Isaac and Jacob I appeared as El Shaddai, but I did not make my name Yahweh known to them".' *(Ex 6:2-3)*

A name can tell us all or tell us nothing. A name can inspire fear or affection, laughter or loneliness, depending on who bears the name. It is the same with the name of God; its significance lies not just in the words but in the One who gives them meaning. The name of God needs the Story to explain it. The word *Yahweh* most likely means 'he is', but can also carry a sense of 'he causes to be' — the One who not only exists himself but makes others exist too. What is in question is a dynamic, creative, caring, yet utterly self-contained presence. In the course of time the name Yahweh was held in such awe that it was never actually pronounced; whenever it occurred in reading, the word *Adonai* (Lord) was substituted so that the sacred Name of God was not spoken. This practice is continued in most English translations; the *(New)* Jerusalem Bible, however, uses 'Yahweh' whenever it occurs in the original Hebrew text.

To *call upon* his name (Ps 80:19), to *seek* his name (83:17), to *praise* his name (Ps 142:8) is to trust and delight in the One who hears the cry and acts in a pattern of constant pity for us. To *know* the name of God is to acknowledge who he is and commit oneself to him.

The many names of God

Psalm 91 opens with four names of God in as many lines (two of them are repeated in v 9):

> *Elyon*
> 'Most High' Both Melchizedek and Abraham worshipped God under this name (Gn 14:17-24).
>
> *Shaddai*
> 'Almighty', or perhaps better, '(God) of the mountain' or '(God) of the wasteland'. The name seems to have come from Mesopotamia, and was used by Abraham's family (see Genesis 17:1; Exodus 6:2).
>
> *Yahweh/Adonai*
> The sacred name revealed to Moses (Ex 3:13-15). It was never actually pronounced; instead the word Lord (*Adonai*) was used.
>
> *Elohim*
> The common title, God. It is a plural form, 'gods', but is used of *one* deity in much the same way as an eminent person such as a king or a pope might refer to himself in the plural — we' or 'us'. (the so-called 'royal plural').

This invoking of God by name and title has an enormous effect in the psalm, like a solid foundation laid beneath the wild imagery that is to follow (vv 3-6). Knowing the name of God (see v 14) refers particularly to *Yahweh*, the name revealed to Moses — the Exodus name.

Psalm 91 is a psalm based on knowing the name of God:

Teacher:

1. He who dwells in the shelter of the *Most High*
   and abides in the shade of the *Almighty*
2. says to the *Lord*: 'My refuge
   my stronghold, my *God* in whom I trust!'

> Elyon
> Shaddai
> Yahweh/Adonai
> Elohim

3. It is he who will free you from the snare
   of the fowler who seeks to destroy you;
4. he will conceal you with his pinions
   and under his wings you will find refuge.

A teaching: trust in God
vv 3-4 God is an eagle
(Deuteronomy 32:11; and see
Psalms 17:8; 124:7)

5. You will not fear the terror of the night
   nor the arrow that flies by day,
6. nor the plague that prowls in the darkness,
   nor the scourge that lays waste at noon.

vv 5-6 God is Lord of day
and night (see Genesis
1:3-5, 14-19)

7. A thousand may fall at your side,
   ten thousand fall at your right,
   you it will never approach;
4c. his faithfulness is buckler and shield.

vv 7-8 God is a warrior
(Ex 14:14)

8. Your eyes have only to look
   to see how the wicked are repaid,
9. you who have said: '*Lord*, my refuge!'
   and have made the *Most High* your dwelling.

> Yahweh/Adonai
> Elyon

10. Upon you no evil shall fall,
    no plague approach where you dwell.
11. For you has he commanded his angels,
    to keep you in all your ways.
12. They shall bear you upon their hands
    lest you strike your foot against a stone.
13. On the lion and the viper you will tread
    and trample the young lion and the dragon.

Prophet:

14. His love he set on me, so I will rescue him;
    protect him for he knows my name.
15. When he calls I shall answer: 'I am with you'.
    I will save him in distress and give him glory.
16. With length of life I will content him;
    I shall let him see my saving power.

ORACLE — *God speaks*

Note the *shape* of Psalm 91 — there are two voices, two parts in the psalm: vv 1-13 is a teaching evoking trust in God, sung by a soloist, or possibly a choir. Although coming first, this section is in fact a commentary on the second part of the psalm. Vv 14-16 is a prophetic statement, spoken on behalf of God, guaranteeing his protection to the one who 'knows my name'.

A sequence of images: The psalmist draws on some traditional elements to express the extent of God's protection, producing a dramatic series of contrasting images. The escape from the trap of the bird-catcher (vv 3-4) is linked with an old image of God as an eagle:

> Like an eagle watching its nest,
> hovering over its young,
> he spreads out his wings to hold him,
> he supports him on his pinions.   *Dt 32:11*

The image is an Exodus one too: 'You have seen for yourselves what I did to the Egyptians and how I carried you away on eagle's wings and brought you to me' (*Ex 19:4*). There is a sudden transition to an entirely new concept: the terrors that roam the world by day and by night are no match for the Creator God who guards every moment: he made and named both day and night (vv 5-6. See Genesis 1:3-5, 14-19). Again the picture abruptly changes: the dying and the dead lie all around, but 'you it will never approach. . . your eyes have only to look' (*vv 7-8*). God will do the fighting for you (see Exodus 14:13-14). All this, because the psalmist knows God's name! The list of dangers continues: plague, lions, snakes, dragons. Knowing the name makes for a calm, a stillness in the soul; in danger from enemies and animals, in the midst of death and darkness, 'all you need to do is to keep calm' (*Ex 14:14*).

In verses 14-16 a prophet speaks, proclaiming God's word: God will answer the one who cries to him by being with him: that is the meaning of his Name.

Exercise 25:   *Enact Psalm 91. Can you dramatise or mime the different images used in the psalm (vv 3-8), and the attitude of one who 'knows the name'?*

                       This is a favourite night prayer in the tradition of the Church; are there times in your life when you might wish to pray this psalm?

2.6 THE END OF THE STORY

The Psalms celebrate the fulfilment of God's promises in the unfolding story of the People of Israel. Each generation had its own experience of God's love and faithfulness: for the people in Egypt it was the release from slavery; for the next generation it was the entry to the land of Canaan; for the people of David's time it was the establishment of the House of David; for the exiles in Babylon it was the return home; and always it was the constant protection of a small nation in the face of overwhelming enemies.

Each year the promise was fulfilled at harvest-time: the land and all that grew on it, crops and cattle, were God's gift. And so, at harvest-time they acknowledged the gift and made an offering to God of the first of all the fruit of the land. And as they did so, they made a profession of faith, they recited a creed that was a story:

> My father was a wandering Aramaean, who went down to Egypt with a small group of men, and stayed there, until he became a great, powerful and numerous nation. The Egyptians ill-treated us, they oppressed us and inflicted harsh slavery on us. But we called on Yahweh, God of our ancestors. Yahweh heard our voice and saw our misery, our toil and our oppression; and Yahweh brought us out of Egypt with mighty hand and outstretched arm, with great terror and with signs and wonders. He brought us here and has given us this country, a country flowing with milk and honey. Hence, I now bring the first-fruits of the soil that you, Yahweh, have given me.   *Dt 26:5-10*

It is the Story again, but not just a tale of days gone by, of great things done long ago. The farmer with his first-fruits *is part of* the Exodus, the first-fruits are his sharing in the promise God made to Israel. And so, generations later, he could identify with those who had suffered in Egypt: he speaks of 'us' and 'we' and 'our' — 'Yahweh brought *us* out of Egypt.' Each fulfilment of the promise is for its own time, whether the farmer with his harvest or the people saved from their enemies. The Story is constantly retold and renewed in the liturgy and feasts of Israel, and in the Psalms, the songs of Israel.

And it is in another set of songs that we find the first hints of where this story might be leading and what are the full dimensions of God's love and faithfulness: the *Song of Mary* (Lk 1:46-55), the *Song of Zechariah* (Lk 1:68-79), and the *Song of Simeon* (Lk 2:29-32). For each of them, the coming of Christ was the fulfilment of promise. Mary sang:

> He protects Israel his servant,
> remembering his mercy,
> the mercy promised to our fathers,
> to Abraham and his sons for ever.   *Lk 1:54-55*

For Zechariah, the Lord, the God of Israel, is to be blessed because he has redeemed his people, 'as he promised':

> He has raised up for us a mighty saviour
> in the house of David his servant,
> as he promised by the lips of holy men,
> those who were his prophets from of old.   *Lk 1:69-70*

And the promise referred to by Simeon (*Lk 2:29*) is surely more than the private assurance given to him that he personally would see the Christ before he died; it is the promise of a salvation for all nations, light for the Gentiles, glory for Israel (see Luke 2:30-32).

These songs are set squarely in the Story of Israel. What is taking place is in continuity with what God 'swore to our father Abraham' (*Lk 1:73*). In a sense, this is the end of the story, what the story has been leading to all these years and generations, only now being revealed that 'it is the God of Abraham, Isaac and Jacob, the God of our ancestors, who has glorified his servant Jesus. . .' (see Acts 3:13). Yet, if there is continuity with the old, there is also something utterly new in this fulfilment, a new story to be remembered and handed on from one generation to the next:

> I want to make quite clear to you, brothers, what the message of the gospel that I preached to you is; you accepted it and took your stand on it, and you are saved by it. . . . The tradition I handed on to you in the first place, a tradition which I had myself received, was that Christ died for our sins, in accordance with the scriptures, and that he was buried; and that on the third day, he was raised to life, in accordance with the scriptures; and that he appeared to Cephas; and later to the Twelve. . . .   *1 Co 15:1-5*

Three things to note:

Firstly, the Gospel is a story, the core of the story of all that was done by and in Jesus. Around this core will be assembled the 'Gospels according to —' Mark and Matthew and Luke and John: the other details and events and significance of Jesus' birth and life, his words and works, his appearances after the Resurrection, his sending of the Spirit, the growth of the Church. It is all the Gospel, the Good News, the Story of what God has done for us.

Secondly, it is a story to be told, to be handed on by one generation and received by the next: Paul teaches what he has been taught himself. Even Cephas (Peter) and the Twelve, the very witnesses to the Risen Lord, themselves received the story: they did not invent it — it is God who tells it. And it is 'in accordance with the scriptures', the continuation of God's will seen in his love and faithfulness to his people Israel.

Thirdly, it is not just a story to be listened to, it is a story to which we belong. It is *our* story: 'Christ died for *our* sins.' Later in the same chapter of 1 Corinthians, Paul talks of 'first-fruits': 'Christ has been raised from the dead, as the first-fruits of all who have fallen asleep. . . in Christ all will be brought to life; but all of them in their proper order: Christ the first-fruits, and next, at his coming, those who belong to him.' (see 1 Corinthians 15:20-23). We belong to Christ — we belong to the Story. And it is celebrated with new songs, and a new Name.

33

Philippians 2:6-11   The pattern of God's pity in a new song

6. (Jesus), being in the form of God,
   did not count equality with God
   something to be grasped.

7. But he emptied himself,
   taking the form of a slave,
   becoming as human beings are;

8. and being in every way like a human being,
   he was humbler yet,
   even to accepting death, death on a cross.

THE HUMAN NEED:
*Jesus takes on himself the
condition of need of all
creation, including the
ultimate need of death.*

9. And for this God raised him high,
   and gave him the name
   which is above all other names;

10. so that all beings
    in the heavens, on earth and in the underworld,
    should bend the knee at the name of Jesus

11. and that every tongue should acknowledge
    Jesus Christ as Lord,
    to the Glory of God the Father.

GOD'S RESPONSE:
*God responds to this need
by raising Jesus to glory.*

This hymn was probably used at Baptism ceremonies in the early Church; it explores the meaning of Christ's death and resurrection. Part of that meaning has to do with the pattern of God's pity that we have already seen in the Psalms and in the story of Israel; the same pattern can be seen in this song. Jesus, though 'equal with God', became a slave, 'becoming as human beings are'. His ultimate slavery was to death — he shared this last need of all humanity. But God responded to the need in Jesus' death by raising him up — not only from the dead, but so that all would acknowledge his *name*. 'Jesus Christ as Lord' — this Lord (in Greek, *Kyrios*) corresponds to the Hebrew *Adonai*. This is, of course, a direct reference to the name of God revealed to the people of Israel. The hymn, then, celebrates the death and resurrection of Jesus — a new song for a new story.

Exercise 26:   *The People of Israel shaped their prayers around the story of God's saving deeds; so do we, particularly in that memorial of the death and resurrection of Jesus that we call the Mass. Read* Eucharistic Prayer IV. *What elements of the Story can you find there? Now look at the other Eucharistic Prayers — what do they tell of the Story? (Note especially what follows the consecration of the bread and wine.) Does the Rosary tell the Story? Why do we recall these events?*

Exercise 27:   *In view of all we have seen about the Story, perhaps it would be useful to review* Exercise 20, *where you told your own story. Is there anything you would like to add? Where does your story begin? Where do you think it might end?*

3 THE CITY AND THE PSALMS

The city of Jerusalem played a central part in the story of the People of Israel. In this chapter we will see something of Jerusalem's history, and some of the psalms connected with the city. We shall also explore the significance of the city for the People of Israel, and for us.

3.1 JOURNEY'S END

The end of the Exodus came not with the entry of the people into the Promised Land, but two centuries later with the arrival in the Ark in Jerusalem. As tradition has it, the Ark was a box made to contain 'the two stone tablets Moses had placed in it at Horeb, the tablets of the Covenant' (see 1 Kings 8:9, and Exodus 25:10-22 where there are instructions on how the Ark was to be made). As related in Numbers 10:33-36, the Ark was carried before the people in their journey through the desert, and preceded them when they crossed the Jordan to enter the land of Canaan (Joshua 3:1-17). For many decades it was kept at Shiloh (1 Samuel 3:3, 21) and was once captured by the Philistines (1 Samuel 4:1-7:1). The references in the grid below take up the story:

Exercise 28:   *The following selection of texts from various books of the Bible outlines the history of events from the capture of the Ark by the Philistines to its eventual placement in a specially built Temple in Jerusalem. Please read them, and for each text write out the main points of that part of the story in the space provided.*

---

1 Samuel 4:1-7:1

---

1 Samuel 8-11

---

1 Samuel 17:1-18:16

---

1 Samuel 31:1-13
2 Samuel 1:1-27

---

2 Samuel 5:1-12

___

2 Samuel 6:1-22

___

1 Kings 6:1-14

___

1 Kings 8:1-13

___

The most significant moment in this story was David's bringing of the Ark into the city of Jerusalem. (Solomon's building of a Temple to house the Ark was simply an extension of David's work.) By that one act the political and religious aspects of the City were merged: Jerusalem became the civil and the spiritual capital for the Israelites. The family of David would rule there for centuries. In its Temple a whole system of worship and many schools of learning would develop. Psalms would be written and collected there. And for generations the Israelites would remember and celebrate in song and drama the day David brought the Ark into the city.

Psalm 132

All:

1. O Lord, remember David
   and all the hardships he endured,
2. the oath he swore to the Lord,
   his vow to the Strong One of Jacob.
3. 'I will not enter the house where I live
   nor go to the bed where I rest.
4. I will give no sleep to my eyes
   to my eyelids will give no slumber
5. till I find a place for the Lord,
   a dwelling for the Strong One of Jacob.'

> *Plea to God based on David's faithfulness and respect for the ark (see 2 Samuel 7:1-2)*

    Choir:

6. At Ephrata we heard of the ark;
   we found it in the plains of Yearim.
7. 'Let us go to the place of his dwelling;
   let us go to kneel at his footstool'.

      8. Go up, Lord, to the place of your rest,
         you and the ark of your strength.
      9. Your priests shall be clothed with holiness:
         your faithful shall ring out their joy.
    10. For the sake of David your servant
       do not reject your anointed.

> *Dramatic recalling* of the *bringing of the Ark into* Jerusalem (2 Samuel 6) *leading to a prayer for the king*

    Prophet:

11. The Lord swore an oath to David:
    he will not go back on his word:
    'A son, the fruit of your body,
    will I set upon your throne.

> *Prophetic response recalling Psalm 89:20-38, God's promise to the House of David*

36

12. If they keep my covenant in truth
    and my laws that I have taught them,
    their sons also shall rule
    on your throne from age to age'.

13. For the Lord has chosen Zion;
    he has desired it for his dwelling:

14. 'This is my resting-place for ever,
    here have I chosen to live.

15. I will greatly bless her produce,
    I will fill her poor with bread.

16. I will clothe her priests with salvation
    and her faithful shall ring out their joy.

17. There the stock of David will flower:
    I will prepare a lamp for my anointed.

18. I will cover his enemies with shame
    but on him my crown shall shine'.

*Another reassurance for the
king: God has chosen Sion.
(Ps 69:16-18; 76:2-4)*

There is a lot of activity and movement in Psalm 132. Its purpose is to invoke the blessing of God on the king in Jerusalem, and it does this by recalling that the king is of David's family, and so the heir to God's guarantee to the House of David (see 2 Samuel 7, and Psalm 89). The story is told on two levels. At the level of history, the psalm recalls and even re-enacts (vv 6-10) how David brought the Ark into the City, and God's promise made to him as a result (vv 11-12, and see 2 Samuel 6, 7).

At a deeper level, however, the psalm reveals that all this — City and King — are *God's* doing: 'For the *Lord has chosen* Zion' (*v 11ff*). It is from God, not from David, that the City gets its holiness. Mount Zion, on which Jerusalem was built, is 'the mountain where God has chosen to dwell' (*Ps 68:17*). He has 'set up his tent in Jerusalem and his dwelling place in Zion' (*Ps 76:3*). So it was not because David brought the Ark into Jerusalem that God is to be found there; rather it was the presence of God there that gave meaning to David's actions. This is the final and best assurance of all, that God has *chosen* to make Jerusalem his 'resting place for ever' (*v 14*). Because of that, 'the stock of David will flower' (*vv 13-18*).

Exercise 29:   *Enact Psalm 132. How would you suggest that vv 6-10 might be acted so
                   as to bring out the excitement of bringing the Ark into the City? Where do
                   you think God's 'resting place' is in our time? Where does he choose to
                   dwell now? Still in Jerusalem?*

3.2 THE SONGS OF ZION

In the life of the Hebrews, Jerusalem (or Zion) became the centre of an enormous affection and admiration. It was a place of wonder, the place where God was to be most eagerly and most surely sought. Inevitably it figured in the song-book of Israel: the 'Songs of Zion' were not just the many psalms that were sung there, but the songs that told of the city itself. Or, more accurately, the songs of God's love for the city.

Psalm 76   God is the defender of his city

   Leader:

1. God is made known in Judah;
   in Israel his name is great.

2. He set up his tent in Jerusalem
   and his dwelling place in Sion.

3. It was there he broke the flashing arrows,
   the shield, the sword, the armour.

*He reminds the people that
God has fought for his city
— perhaps the defeat of the
Assyrians (see 2 Kings
19:10-35)*

People:

4. You, O Lord, are resplendent,
   more majestic than the everlasting mountains.
5. The warriors, despoiled, slept in death;
   the hands of the soldiers were powerless.
6. At your threat, O God of Jacob,
   horse and rider lay stunned.
7. You, you alone, strike terror.
   Who shall stand when your anger is roused?
8. You uttered your sentence from the heavens;
   the earth in terror was still
9. when God arose to judge,
   to save the humble of the earth
10. Men's anger will serve to praise you;
    its survivors surround you in joy.

They sing a song of victory over the enemy without. But God is judge within the city too; only the 'humble of the earth' can be at ease with him

Leader:

11. Make vows to your God and fulfil them.
    Let all pay tribute to him who strikes terror.
12. who cuts short the breath of princes,
    who strikes terror in the kings of the earth.

A warning to the people and the king — be faithful to God!

God defends his city and its people against their enemies, whether these are attacking armies or oppressors within the city. The ruler on the throne of David is also one of the 'kings of the earth' — he too will be judged by the God who saves the poor and the humble.

God's defence of his city against enemy forces becomes part of the wonder of Jerusalem, as we can see in Psalm 48:

Psalm 48   The Ballad of the Splendid City

2. The Lord is great and worthy to be praised
   in the city of our God.
3. His holy mountain rises in beauty,
   the joy of all the earth.
   Mount Sion, true pole of the earth,
   the Great King's city!

Praise of God in a new geography: Mount Zion is the greatest of the world's mountains (see Psalm 68:16-17)

4. God, in the midst of its citadels,
   has shown himself its stronghold,
5. For the kings assembled together,
   together they advanced.
6. They saw; at once they were astounded;
   dismayed, they fled in fear.
7. A trembling seized them there,
   like the pangs of birth.
8. By the east wind you have destroyed
   the ships of Tarshish.
9. As we have heard, so we have seen
   in the city of our God,
   in the city of the Lord of hosts
   which God upholds for ever.

Telling the story: God's defence of his city against enemies (see Psalms 46:4-7; 76:1-3; Isaiah 7:1-9; (2 Kings 19:10-35) They had heard the stories; now that they have seen the city they know the stories must be true.

10. O God, we ponder your love
    within your temple.
11. Your praise, O God, like your name
    reaches the ends of the earth.
    With justice your right hand is filled.

In the quiet of the Temple they can contemplate all they have seen and heard of God's love and justice in the city.

12. Mount Sion rejoices;
    the people of Judah rejoice
    at the sight of your judgements.

13. Walk through Sion, walk all round it;
    count the number of its towers.
14. Review all its ramparts,
    examine its castles,
    that you may tell the next generation
15. that such is our God,
    our God for ever and always.
    It is he who leads us.

*(A 'stage direction' —
see Chapter 1.10) Walking
about the city, savouring
the sights. Tell them back
home…*

This psalm captures the experience of the pilgrim-tourist: admiring the magnificence of Jerusalem, hearing the summarised account of its survival through many wars and sieges, pondering in the prayerful quiet of the Temple, seeing all the city sights. And when he goes home, the tales he will have to tell!

Psalm 46   God is our stronghold

This psalm praises God who is our 'refuge and strength.' He is the very-present God, close at hand, within the City. The refrain (vv 8 and 12, and supplied in v 4) sets the theme:

> The Lord of hosts is with us:
> the God of Jacob is our stronghold.

In three images the psalm explores what this presence of God means.

vv 1-4   God is a helper in time of distress, and what could be more distressful for a city than an earthquake? Yet even if an earthquake should happen — and earth rocks and mountains fall and waters rage — we need not fear. God, who created all things, can save us even in the rubble of a ruined city — or of a ruined life.

vv 5-8   The psalmist sings of 'the waters of a river' — but there is no river in Jerusalem: the city drew its water from deep pools and springs (2 Kings 20:20). It is only for prophets that a river rises in the Temple to give life to the land (see Ezekiel 47:1-12; Zechariah 14:8, and Revelation 22:1-2). The psalmist, too, looks forward to the Day of the Lord when enemy nations and kingdoms no longer threaten the city — for God is within it.

vv 9-12   The scene changes yet again,and broadens out over all the earth. God brings peace and an end to wars. The tranquillity of his presence, already known in the city, will be felt throughout the whole world: 'Be still and know that I am God.' There is a prophetic hope in the psalm, based on God's presence in Zion. To truly know God is to know his presence in ourselves — and be still!

Psalms 46, 48 and 76 all speak of the strong presence of God to defend his city. And indeed, the people of Israel and their capital city had many enemies — Psalm 83 (as we saw in Chapter 2.4) envisaged the land ringed around by hostile nations. But there was another vision in the prophets and in the Psalms, a different hope for the City in the midst of the nations:

It will happen in the final days
that the mountain of Yahweh's house
will rise higher than the mountains
and tower above the heights.
Then all the nations will stream to it,
many peoples will come to it and say,
'Come, let us go up to the mountain of Yahweh,
to the house of the God of Jacob
that he may teach us his ways
so that we may walk in his paths.'
For the Law will issue from Zion
and the word of Yahweh from Jerusalem.   *Is 2:2-3*

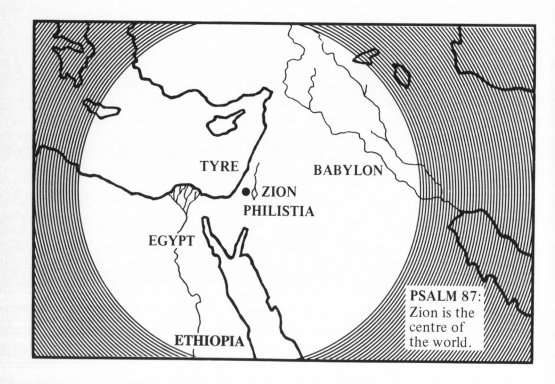

TYRE

BABYLON

●◊ ZION

PHILISTIA

EGYPT

PSALM 87:
Zion is the
centre of
the world.

ETHIOPIA

Psalm 87 Zion is the Mother of all the nations — even the old enemies!

Choir:
1. On the holy mountain is his city
   cherished by the Lord.
2. The Lord prefers the gates of Zion
   to all Jacob's dwellings.

The LORD has chosen Zion

Prophet:

> 3. Of you are told glorious things,
>   O city of God!
> 4. Babylon and Egypt I will count
>   among those who know me;
>   Philistia, Tyre, Ethiopia,
>   these will be her children
> 5a. and Zion shall be called 'Mother'
>   for all shall be her children.

Prophetic vision (see Isaiah 2:2-3): Zion will be the Mother of all the nations, including even the ancient enemies! Thus says the LORD. . . (see map.)

Choir:

5b. It is he, the Lord Most High,
    who gives each his place.
 6. In his register of peoples he writes:
    'These are her children'
 7. and while they dance they will sing:
    'In you all fnd their home.'

Continuing the praise of God in response to the prophetic word: God will bring all peoples home to Zion.

The Lord has indeed chosen Zion, but this choice was not intended to exclude the peoples of the world, but instead to attract them to himself. In the end, the City of God is home for all of us. God is to be found in Jerusalem, but he is not confined there.

Exercise 30:   *Read the following texts:*
    Isaiah 60:1-22   *Prophetic hopes for a restored Jerusalem.*
    Acts of the Apostles 2:1-13   *People from all lands gather for Pentecost*
                  in Jerusalem.
    Revelation 21:1-22:2   *The vision of the heavenly Jerusalem. Jerusalem/Zion continued to be part of the story down to our own day, not only for the Jews, but for Christians and Muslims also. And it helps to express our hopes for the future. What does Jerusalem mean to you?*

3.3 NEXT YEAR IN JERUSALEM

With the building of the Temple to house the Ark of the Covenant, the City of Jerusalem was established for the Israelites as the spiritual centre of the world. People began to come there on pilgrimage. Truly, God could be sought anywhere, but Jerusalem, the City of God, was especially sacred to him. It was his dwelling place, and a desirable place to be.

Psalm 84   In which the singer traces the many aspects of pilgrimage.

2. How lovely is your dwelling place,
    Lord, God of hosts.
3. My soul is longing and yearning,
    is yearning for the courts of the Lord.
    My heart and my soul ring out their joy
    to God, the living God.

Desire to be in the place where God is — the beginning of all pilgrimage.

4. The sparrow herself finds a home
    and the swallow a nest for her brood;
    she lays her young by your altars,
    Lord of hosts, my king and my God.
5. They are happy who dwell in your house,
    for ever singing your praise.

Jerusalem is home; this is where we belong. Pilgrimage brings a sense of home-coming.

6. They are happy, whose strength is in you,
in whose hearts are the roads to Sion.
7. As they go through the Bitter Valley
they make it a place of springs
(the autumn rain covers it with blessings).
8. They walk with ever growing strength,
they will see the God of Gods in Sion.

Journey: all roads lead to Zion, if the desire is in one's heart. To go on such a journey is to bring a blessing (signified by the life-giving rains).

9. O Lord God of hosts, hear my prayer,
give ear, O God of Jacob.
10. Turn your eyes, O God, our shield,
look on the face of your anointed.
11. One day within your courts
is better than a thousand elsewhere.
The threshold of the house of God
I prefer to the dwellings of the wicked.
12. For the Lord God is a rampart, a shield;
he will give us his favour and glory.
The Lord will not refuse any good
to those who walk without blame.
13. Lord God of hosts,
happy the man who trusts in you.

Arrival: a prayer for the king ('your anointed', v 10) now that the pilgrims are in Jerusalem. But the real King is God — this is his city, his house: a place of blessing and safety. The pilgrim's desire is fulfilled: he is with God.

The psalm describes some of the main aspects of going on pilgrimage: it is based on a *desire* to be close to God in his holy place; that place is, in fact, our *home* — we belong there; but we must *journey* to our home, and sometimes the travelling is hard and bitter; yet how wonderful is the *arrival* — it is good to be here!

Exercise 31:   *In small groups: listen as one person reads Psalm 84 slowly. Think prayerfully about its meaning for you and your life. Share in the group: are we on pilgrimage? What is our destination? What about the journey? From your meditation and sharing, can you say if any part of the psalm speaks to your heart?*

Apart from daily sacrifices in the Temple, with special services on the Sabbath and on the first day of each month, the calendar for the Israelites was marked by three major festivals: the combined feasts of *Passover* and *Unleavened Bread,* the feast of *Weeks* (which followed Unleavened Bread by seven weeks, or fifty days — from which it got its later name of Pentecost), and the feast of *Tabernacles* (or Tents), the most important of the three, and often called simply, The Feast.

> *Three times a year all your menfolk must appear before Yahweh your God in the place chosen by him: at the feast of Unleavened Bread, at the feast of Weeks, at the feast of Shelters. No one must appear empty-handed before Yahweh, but each must give what he can, in proportion to the blessing which Yahweh your God has bestowed on you.   Dt 16:16-17*

These feasts had their origins in some of the special times in the lives of the farmers and nomadic herdsmen in the land of Canaan and the surrounding countries: the time of planting, of harvest, of setting out with herds and flocks for new pastures. These are all times when people asked for God's special blessing, and gave him thanks for his goodness. In time, the original significance of the feasts was forgotten; the feasts were still celebrated, but now they were seen as commemorating special events in the story of Israel's liberation.

Month	Name of Feast	Origins	New Meaning
January			
February			
March	PASSOVER & UNLEAVENED BREAD	*Pastoral:* herdsmen setting out for new pastures *Agricultural:* barley harvest begins	EXODUS & DEATH OF FIRST-BORN (Deuteronomy 16:1-8; Leviticus 23:5-8)
April			
May	WEEKS (or Pentecost)	*Agricultural:* end of wheat harvest	MOUNT SINAI: COVENANT & LAW (Deuteronomy 16:9-12; Leviticus 23:15-22)
June			
July			
August			
September	TABERNACLES (or Tents)	*Agricultural:* fruit harvest (grapes & olives)	DESERT WANDERING, LIVING IN TENTS. (Deuteronomy 16:13-15; Leviticus 23:33-36)
October			
November			
December			

Psalm 122

After the long journey, a pilgrim rejoices at his safe arrival, and marvels at the City (vv 1-3). The tribes converge on Jerusalem to worship there and to pay respect to the 'house of David' (vv 4-5). This gathering of brothers and sisters, overcoming all tribal barriers, is a sign of unity for all peoples, and greetings are exchanged: 'Peace be to your homes!'. . . . 'Peace upon you!' (vv 6-9). Jerusalem is the city of peace (Salem, another traditional name for the city, was seen to echo *Shalom*, the Hebrew word for peace.)

Psalm 133

Recognises the same blessing of peace and unity to be found in Jerusalem:

> How good and how pleasant it is,
> when brothers live in unity! (*v 1*)

The oil flowing on the anointed priest (see Psalm 84:10) of the family of Aaron leads to an image of the whole city anointed with dew! (vv 2-3). This water of life is truly a blessing from God. To celebrate the festivals in Jerusalem was to be blessed by God.

Both these psalms come from a group of fifteen psalms (120-134) each of which bears the title, 'Song of Ascents'. This group seems to have been associated with pilgrimage to Jerusalem, and may have formed a collection of songs suitable for the journey up to the city.

Pilgrimage to Jerusalem was, then, an important aspect of life and worship for the people of Israel. By coming together to celebrate the great events in their story, they were being renewed in their faith. And so it continued for centuries: 'Every year his parents used to go to Jerusalem for the feast of Passover. When he was twelve years old, they went up for the feast as usual. . . . (*Lk 2:41ff*). St John's Gospel puts Jesus in Jerusalem on several occasions for the feasts of Passover (2:13; 11:55) and Tabernacles (7:2 and possibly 5:1). For hundreds of years before the birth of Christ the Israelites had been spreading to neighbouring countries. Later, even more were dispersed all over the world. Always, however, there were in their hearts 'the roads to Zion' (*Ps 84:6*). Each year as they celebrated the Passover Meal in their homes, the hope arose afresh that soon, perhaps even the following year, they would be standing 'within your gates, O Jerusalem' (*Ps 122:2*). The Meal ended with the wish: 'Next year in Jerusalem!'

Exercise 32:   *Why do people go on pilgrimages today — to Jerusalem, Rome, Lourdes, Mecca?*
Can you suggest some good reasons for going on pilgrimage? To find God, is it necessary to go on pilgrimage?

3.4 SEEK THE FACE OF THE LORD

The Ark of the Covenant, the Temple, the succession of pilgrimages — all these underlined the fact that Jerusalem was the place where God could be found. 'You must seek Yahweh your God only in the place he himself will choose from among all your tribes, to set his name there and give it a home' (*Dt 12:5*). To the suggestion that God should be sought elsewhere Amos replied:

> For Yahweh says this to the House of Israel,
> seek me and you shall live.
> Do not seek Bethel,
> do not go to Gilgal,
> do not journey to Beersheba,
> since Gilgal is going to be exiled
> and Bethel brought to nothing.
> Seek Yahweh and you shall live   *Am 5:4-5*

Originally, then, to 'seek the Lord' meant to go to his Temple in Jerusalem and consult him there. There was a *geographical* emphasis on Jerusalem to strengthen its religious and political supremacy.

However, behind the technical sense of consulting Yahweh at the Temple, there was another meaning to Amos' words, 'Seek Yahweh and you shall live'. The Book of Deuteronomy suggests that life is a seeking after God, 'and if you seek him with all your heart and with all your soul, you shall find him' (*4:29*). The truth is that God is always and everywhere present: this is the meaning of his name (see Chapter 2.5). One cannot speak of God's presence as if he could be absent. Yet, even though God is constantly *here*, he needs to be looked for. And so the psalms that speak of going to Jerusalem to find God there, also tell of our need to search for him wherever we are, and within ourselves.

Psalm 27

seems to express both levels of longing for God. (Experts debate whether this was originally one psalm or two: vv 1-6 and 7-14.)

27:1-6

The psalmist is threatened by 'evil-doers . . . enemies and foes', even an army encamping against him (*vv 2-3*. Is it perhaps the king who is speaking?). He turns in confidence to God, his light and help and stronghold (v 1). But specifically he asks,

'to live in the house of the Lord,
all the days of my life,
to savour the sweetness of the Lord,
to behold his temple.'   *v 4*

It is there, within God's 'tent' (*vv 5-6*) that he will be safe from 'my foes who surround me'. This is the kind of desire to be close to God in his Temple that gives rise to pilgrimage.

27:7-14

The psalmist is again (or still) harassed by enemies and 'false witnesses' (*v 11*), and again he appeals to God:

O Lord, hear my voice when I call;
have mercy and answer.
Of you my heart has spoken:
'Seek his face.'
It is your face, O Lord, that I seek;
hide not your face.   *vv 7-8*

Here there is something more than a desire to find protection against enemies or to stand in the Holy City of God. This is the heart's longing to look into the eyes of God. The singer has a great fear of being separated from God, the fright of a child forsaken by its father and mother (vv 9-10, and see Isaiah 49:15). But he is sure of God (vv 13-14) and of his blessing:

May Yahweh bless you and keep you.
May Yahweh let his face shine on you and be gracious to you.
May Yahweh show you his face and bring you peace.   *N 6:24-26*

The two parts of the psalm highlight different aspects of the desire for God. In the end we learn that God will be found in the Temple if he is also being sought in one's own heart; and the heart's desire can be expressed by one's feet: the journey to Jerusalem tells of our going to God.

Pilgrimage begins with a thirst in the soul. The title of Psalm 63 sets it in the life of David, 'when he was in the desert of Judah' (and see 1 Samuel 22-24). The desert surroundings, parched for rain, become a landscape of longing:

O God, you are my God, for you I long;
for you my soul is thirsting.
My body pines for you
like a dry, weary land without water.
So I gaze on you in the sanctuary
to see your strength and your glory.   *Ps 63:2-3*

In the desert, away from Jerusalem, he feels absent from God, bodily separated from him: 'My soul is thirsting for you, my flesh is longing for you' (v 2, JB). There is a similar thirst in Psalms 42-43.

Psalms 42-43

In fact, these are a single psalm, though they are separated in most bibles. The psalm is a cry of anguish from an exile so far removed from Jerusalem and the Temple that he can be challenged as not having a God at all:

> My enemies revile me,
> saying to me all the day long:
> 'Where is your God?'   (see 42:4,10-11;43:2)

His desire is for 'the rejoicing crowd in the house of God' (42:5), for the 'altar of God, the God of my joy' (43:4). From the distance of Mount Hermon he longs for another height; the 'holy mountain' where God dwells (43:3). He is far from the *place* where God dwells, where he once found and praised him:

> My soul is thirsting for God,
> the God of my life;
> when can I enter and see
> the face of God?   42:3

This is a very physical, bodily desire for God-in-a-place. Yet there is a refrain, repeated three times in the psalm, that seems to express a deeper hope: even if he is far removed from the *place* where God dwells, he is not removed from *God* nor from praising God:

> Why are you cast down, my soul,
> why groan within me?
> Hope in God; I will praise him still,
> my saviour and my God.   42:6,12;43:5

The experience of exile is helping to free the psalmist from slavery to a place or a building. God is present in every place and time:

The woman said, 'Our Fathers worshipped on this mountain, through you say that Jerusalem is the place where one ought to worship'. Jesus said:
> 'Believe me, woman, the hour is coming
> when you will worship the Father
> neither on this mountain nor in Jerusalem.
> You worship what you do not know;
> we worship what we do know;
> for salvation comes from the Jews.
> But the hour is coming — indeed is already here —
> when true worshippers will worship the Father in spirit and truth:
> that is the kind of worshipper
> the Father seeks.
> God is spirit,
> and those who worship
> must worship in spirit and truth.'   Jn 4:20-24

Exercise 33: *On the map on page 48 please locate the following places:*

Jerusalem	Mount Hermon	River Jordan
Gilgal	Bethel	Beersheba
Shiloh	Dan	

Exercise 34:   *Share in small groups the following questions: write up the questions, and allow each person to choose which group s/he wishes to join:-*

1. *Where do you find it easiest to pray? Can you say why?*
2. *If God can be praised in any place, why do we go to church on Sunday, or on any day?*
3. *Do Psalms 27 or 42-43 speak to any experience in your life? When would you feel like praying one of these psalms?*
4. *Can you recall any time in your life when you felt you were removed very far from God? What were your feelings at that time?*

3.5 THE VIOLENT CITY

Jerusalem was indeed a great city, a centre of culture and learning. In 1 Chronicles 23-27 we can find details of the organisation established by David for the running of the Temple, the army and the civil service. In the reigns of both David and Solomon, the arts flourished — see 1 Chronicles 25, where David appoints people to be in charge of religious music (including the 'sons of Asaph'!). 2 Chronicles 2 describes the gathering of artists and craftsmen who know 'the arts of working in gold, silver, bronze, iron, stone, wood, scarlet, violet, fine linen and crimson materials. . . . competent to carry out any kind of engraving'. Trade expanded enormously with the neighbouring countries (2 Chronicles 9:13-14, 20-28). The fame of the city drew the Queen of Sheba to Jerusalem, and what she saw 'left her breathless, and she said to the king, 'the report I heard in my own country about you and about your wisdom in handling your affairs was true, then!' (see 2 Chronicles 9:1-12). The Queen noted another of the glories of the city, according to Chronicles: 'Because your God loves Israel and means to uphold him forever, he has made you king over them to administer law and justice'.

The king in Jerusalem was indeed consecrated to uphold justice: in a psalm sung by the king he proclaims:

> Morning by morning I will silence
> all the wicked in the land,
> uprooting from the city of the Lord
> all who do evil.   *Ps 101:8*

In the morning court sessions (see 2 Samuel 5:1-6) people were free to come before the king seeking justice: 'There were set the thrones of judgement of the house of David' (*Ps 122:5*). One of the most joyful aspects of the City was the gathering in unity and peace of so many people from so many tribes and nations:

> How good and how pleasant it is
> when brothers live in unity!   *Ps 133:1*

Unfortunately, this version of things, conveyed especially in the Books of Chronicles, does not tell the whole story. There was another experience of the city, as we can see from Psalm 59.

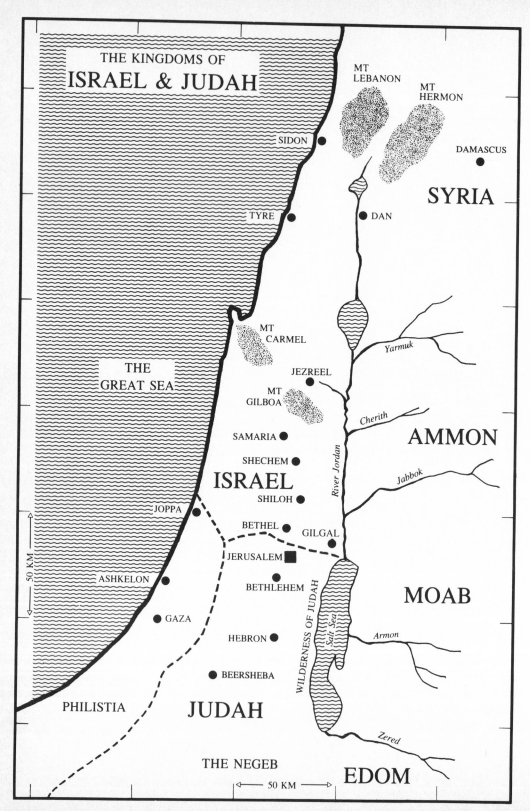

THE KINGDOMS OF
ISRAEL & JUDAH

MT LEBANON

MT HERMON

SIDON

DAMASCUS

SYRIA

TYRE

DAN

MT CARMEL

THE GREAT SEA

JEZREEL

MT GILBOA

Yarmuk

SAMARIA

Cherith

AMMON

SHECHEM

ISRAEL

SHILOH

River Jordan

Jabbok

JOPPA

BETHEL

GILGAL

JERUSALEM

50 KM

ASHKELON

BETHLEHEM

MOAB

GAZA

HEBRON

Salt Sea

Armon

BEERSHEBA

WILDERNESS OF JUDAH

PHILISTIA

JUDAH

Zered

THE NEGEB

EDOM

50 KM

Psalm 59 The Menace of the Night City

2. Rescue me, God, from my foes;
    protect me from those who attack me.
3. O rescue me from those who do evil
    and save me from blood-thirsty men.
4. See, they lie in wait for my life;
    powerful men band together against me.
    For no offence, no sin of mine, Lord,
5. for no guilt of mine they rush to take their stand.
    Awake, come to my aid and see!
6. Lord of hosts, you are Israel's God.
    Rouse yourself and punish the nations;
    show no mercy to evil traitors.

> 7. *Each evening they come back like dogs.*
>   *They howl and roam about the city,*
>   *they prowl in search of food,*
>   *they snarl till they have their fill.*

8. See how they gabble open-mouthed;
    their lips are filled with insults,
    'For who', they say, 'will hear us?'
9. But you, Lord, will laugh them to scorn,
    You make light of all the nations.

> 10. *O my Strength, it is you to whom I turn,*
>   *for you, O God, are my stronghold,*
> 11. *the God who shows me love.*

    O God, come to my aid
    and let me look in triumph on my foes,
12. God, kill them lest my people be seduced;
    rout them by your power, lay them low.
    It is you, O Lord, who are our shield.
13. For the sins of their mouths and their lips,
    for the curses and lies that they speak
    let them be caught in their pride.
14. Destroy them, Lord, in your anger.
    Destroy them till they are no more.
    Let men know that God is the ruler
    over Jacob and the ends of the earth.

> 15. *Each evening they come back like dogs.*
>   *They howl and roam about the city,*
> 16. *they prowl in search of food,*
>   *they snarl till they have their fill.*

17. As for me, I will sing of your strength
    and each morning acclaim your love
    for you have been my stronghold,
    a refuge in the day of my distress.

> 18. *O my Strength, it is you to whom I turn,*
>   *for you, O God, are my stronghold,*
>   *the God who shows me love.*

A cry for help: *the singer is surrounded by powerful enemies.*

Refrain A: *As darkness falls, scavenging dogs roam the city streets — like the singer's enemies!*

The enemies: *fools who say there is no God. The singer, however, knows better, and trusts in God.*

Refrain B: *God is my strength, my stronghold, my love.*

Cursing the enemies: *the violence of the city invades the singer himself as fear and hatred give an edge to his anger*

Refrain A: *again, the prowling dogs*

Praise of God *as the morning comes — the dawn breaking over the city is a sign of safety. The dark has passed.*

Refrain B: *the strength of God*

Exercise 35:　　In Psalm 59, the singer is so threatened by his enemies in the city that he begins to react with hatred and violence himself (vv 12-14). In our cities today many live in situations of similar hardship: armed robbery, vandalism, poverty and loneliness, overcrowding, oppressive living conditions, harsh or unjust authorities . . . How do people react to these experiences? Can you recount some incident in your own life when you were harshly or unjustly treated — how did you react? (Share in small groups.)

There are two refrains in Psalm 59. Refrain A (vv 7 and 15-16) takes the image of dogs scouring the streets to describe the singer's experience of his enemies. Refrain B (vv 10-11a and 18) expresses his confidence in God who loves him. The singer is held in tension between these two experiences, and his reaction is to curse his enemies (vv 11b-14). This is one of the worst effects of violence, that it causes its victims to be violent themselves. In Psalm 109 we find the example of someone driven to a frenzy of hatred for his tormentors: they have hounded him with deceit and wickedness, with lying tongues and false accusations until at last his control breaks and he launches the most dreadful curses against the leader of his enemies:

> Let his father's guilt be remembered,
> his mother's sin be retained.
> Let it always stand before the Lord,
> that their memory be cut off from the earth.
> For he did not think of showing mercy
> but pursued the poor and the needy,
> hounding the wretched to death.
>
> He loved cursing; let curses fall upon him.
> He scorned blessing; let blessing pass him by.
> He put on cursing like his coat;
> let it soak into his body like water;
> let it sink like oil into his bones;
> let it be like the clothes that cover him,
> like a girdle he cannot take off!　　(*see Psalm 109:6-19*)

Exercise 36:　　How do you feel about these 'cursing psalms'? Can we use them in our prayer? Would you use violence to protect yourself? — to get your rights? — to punish those who have done wrong?

The danger out of the dark alleyways can drive a person to leave the city entirely, to look for safety far away from human company: at least, that is the advice given to the singer of Psalm 11:

Psalm 11　 The Lord is my stronghold and refuge.

1. In the Lord I have taken my refuge.

The singer's statement of faith and trust

　　How can you say to my soul:
　　'Fly like a bird to its mountain,
2. See the wicked bracing their bow;
　　they are fixing their arrows on the string
　　to shoot upright men in the dark.
3. Foundations once destroyed, what can the just do?'

His friends suggest that he leave the city to escape his enemies.

4. The Lord is in his holy temple,
   the Lord, whose throne is in heaven.
   His eyes look down on the world;
   his gaze tests mortal men.
5. The Lord tests the just and the wicked:
   the lover of violence he hates.
6. He sends fire and brimstone on the wicked;
   he sends a scorching wind as their lot.
7. The Lord is just and loves justice:
   the upright shall see his face.

But he rejects this advice;
to leave the city would be
to leave the presence of
God in the Temple. If God
is in the city that is hope
and protection enough.

The strong faith of Psalms 59 and 11 should not blind us to the immense *courage* they also show. Where corruption and injustice are deeply ingrained, when even the foundations of hope are destroyed, only the brave will stay to face the enemy. It would be so much easier to run away — but even that may not be possible!

In Psalm 55, it is the singer himself who wishes to flee the city; he is filled with disappointment and fear — even more than Psalms 11 or 59, this psalm reflects the singer's feelings of betrayal when he meets with violence in the City.

Psalm 55 'One of you is about to betray me.'

vv 2-12
The psalm opens with a desperately repeated plea for help from a man terrified at the howling fury of his enemies (vv 2-4). His heart twists within him at the presence of death — and he longs to escape like a bird to the desert, where no human dwells, away from lies and plotting tongues (vv 7-9). This is the very experience of the prophet Jeremiah:

Who will find me a wayfarer's shelter
in the desert,
for me to quit my people,
and leave them far behind?
For all of them are adulterers,
a conspiracy of traitors.
They bend their tongues like a bow;

Let each be on his guard against his friend;
do not trust a brother,
for every brother aims but to supplant,
and every friend is a peddler of slander.   *Jr 9:1-3*

The whole city is infected with this evil: where people should live in harmony, in the City of Peace, there is nothing but violence, strife, wickedness, evil, tyranny, deceit (vv 10-12). Where can the singer hope to turn from this bitterness? The whole meaning of Jerusalem is betrayed.

vv 13-24
But this is not some unknown, faceless horror that is poisoning the city; it is not even the work of an enemy or a rival (v 13). But 'it is you, my own companion, my intimate friend' (*v 14*). The fact that they had prayed together in the Temple makes the treachery even more bitter (v 15) and the singer utters a terrible curse on all his enemies (v 16):

May they recoil in disorder,
   may death descend on them,
may they go down alive to Sheol,
   since evil shares their home with them.   (*NJB*)

From this vengeful outburst the singer turns to prayers of confidence in God, crying and lamenting day and night — and God will hear him and bring down his enemies, especially that smooth-talking traitor who turned against his own friends! (vv 17-24)

In the story of the People of Israel, the city of Jerusalem began with great promise. As spiritual, cultural and civil capital, it should have gathered together all that was best in the life of the people. Instead, in the eyes of many, including the prophets, it became a centre for hypocrisy and gross injustice:

> Her leaders give verdicts for presents
> her priests take a fee for their rulings,
> her prophets divine for money.   (see Micah 3:9-12)

There was in the City alienation, loneliness, fear, poverty, crime:

> The faithful city,
> what a harlot she has become!
> Zion, once full of fair judgement,
> where saving justice used to dwell,
> but now assassins!

> Your silver has turned into dross,
> your wine is watered.
> Your princes are rebels,
> accomplices of brigands.

> All of them greedy for presents
> and eager for bribes,
> they show no justice to the orphan,
> and the widow's cause never reaches them.   *Is 1:21-23*

And so it continued:

> As he drew near and came in sight of the city he shed tears over it and said, 'If you too had only recognised on this day the way to peace! But in fact it is hidden from your eyes! Yes, a time is coming when your enemies will raise fortifications all round you, when they will encircle you and hem you in on every side; they will dash you and the children inside your walls to the ground; they will leave not one stone standing on another within you, because you did not recognise the moment of your visitation.   *Lk 19:41-44*

Exercise 37:   *Why do people come to our cities today? Are cities places of friendship and hope? What is your experience of urban life? Can we, ordinary people, do anything to make life in our city more human and pleasant?*

Discussion of these and similar questions may lead the group to a desire for action: can you name people, or some kinds of people, who might suffer special hardships in city life — could you, or this Bible study group, do anything to help them?

3.6   HOW MANY MILES TO BABYLON?

After the death of Solomon, the Kingdom established by David soon divided in two — the Kingdom of *Israel*, with its capital at Samaria in the north, and the Kingdom of *Judah* in the south under the House of David ruling in Jerusalem. (See map on page 48). The northern kingdom survived for 200 years, the southern kingdom for almost 350 years, down to the destruction of Jerusalem in 587 BC, and the Babylonian Captivity.

Exercise 38:   *The following selection of texts continue the story of Jerusalem and the People of Israel from the death of Solomon to the return of the exiles from Babylon. Please read them, and for each text write out the main points of that part of the story in the space provided.*

1 Kings 12	931 BC
1 Kings 18:20-40	c.865 BC
Amos 2:6-8; 4:4-12	c.750 BC
2 Kings 17:5-23	721 BC
Isaiah 1:21-28	c.701 BC
Jeremiah 5:1-6	c.625 BC
2 Kings 25:1-21	c.587 BC
Ezekiel 37:1-14	c.560 BC
Isaiah 40:1-11	c.550 BC
Ezra 1:1-11	538 BC

You will notice from this sequence of texts how many of the prophets belong to this part of Israel's story: Amos, Elijah, Isaiah, Jeremiah, Ezekiel and a great prophet whose name we do not know but whose prophecies are to be found in the Book of Isaiah, chapters 40-55. Also belonging to this period of history are Elisha, Hosea and Micah.

For the faithful Israelites, the destruction of Jerusalem in 587 BC was a devastating experience (see 2 Kings 25:1-21). For all its failure and violence, it was still the beloved city, the symbol of God's presence in defence of his people. When it was destroyed by the Babylonians, the Temple torn down, the King taken captive and blinded and the people deported to Babylon, it seemed as if God himself had failed and betrayed his own people. Perhaps his faithfulness and love did not, after all, endure for ever! The Israelites had lost their land and home; had they also lost their God? Some of the Psalms reflect the anxious questioning of the people as they tried to cope with the disaster that had overtaken them.

Psalm 74   God is to blame!
vv 1-11
The psalmist explores the terrible possibility that God has cast off his own people — this is the real concern of this psalm, not just defeat and destruction by the enemy. He raises no question about the failure or guilt of the *people*: this is straight protest — how can God forget his own people and his own dwelling-place (vv 1-2)? Mention of Zion leads to a description of the dreadful havoc caused by the enemy in the Temple, even in the very sanctuary (vv 3-8). And God has allowed this to happen! For how long will this go on? We have no one to tell us, no sign, no prophet. God is silent (vv 9-11).

vv 12-17

And yet! Through all the anguish and terror, hope survives. The psalmist reaches back to the great saving events of Israel's story, back to confidence in the God who creates and who saves. The dividing of the waters, the crushing of monsters ('Leviathan') in the sea, the control over the springs of water — all these images (vv 13-15) refer to both the Creation and Exodus stories. God is master of all the world, of all times and seasons (vv 16-17). Surely, such a God can re-create Israel and rebuild Jerusalem — even now!

vv 18-23

And so the psalmist returns to his pleas: he appeals to God's name (v 18), his choice of Israel, 'your dove' (*v 19*), the Covenant (v 20), his commitment to 'the poor and the needy' (v 21). In the end, he calls on God to stir himself and do his duty! After all, it is *his* enemies who are destroying Jerusalem (vv 22-23)!

Psalm 79   We have sinned — we and our fathers.

Here we have the same scene as in Psalm 74, but instead of indignation there is a plea for pardon: the cry, 'How long, O Lord?' (*v 5*) here refers to God's anger at the sins of the people (not, as in Psalm 74:10, to the freedom given by God to Israel's enemies). So the destruction of the City is seen to be the result of the unfaithfulness of the people (vv 8-9). It was deserved; they had been warned. Yet, even from guilt there is an appeal to the compassion of God (v 8).

There is here a great understanding of the realities of life: guilt and the need for pardon are, in fact, the strongest of all reasons for calling on God's name:

> O Lord our God, forgive us our sins;
> rescue us for the sake of your name.   *v 9*

He is the God who listens even to the sinner who has no case to make for himself. The destruction of Jerusalem has left them naked to their enemies, but also most open to the ways of God.

The Exile lasted about sixty years. The leaders of the people, the craftsmen and scholars and thousands of others were led away to Babylon (see 2 Kings 24:14-16;25:11). Those left behind (2 Kings 25:12) lived as best they could in the ruins of the city. But there was no more worship or pilgrimage or sacrifice or singing. The long Story seemed to have come to an end at last. The exiles in Babylon were even more torn from their traditions. They had been driven from Temple, city, land — perhaps even from the presence of God? For them too there could be no singing the praises of God in a foreign land. But they did not forget, nor did they allow the story to be forgotten by their children. The length of the Exile meant that very few of the original captives lived to see the City again. But those who did return to Jerusalem knew the story of its destruction, and who the destroyers were. Perhaps it was one of them who wrote the most tragic lament of all, Psalm 137:

Psalm 137   How many miles to Babylon?

1. By the rivers of Babylon
   there we sat and wept,
   remembering Zion;
2. on the poplars that grew there
   we hung up our harps.
3. For it was there that they asked us,
   our captors, for songs,
   our oppressors, for joy.
   'Sing to us,' they said,
   'one of Zion's songs.'

On alien soil: *There is no community, no place for worship, no Story, no Song. The exiles are alienated from all that gave them identity and meaning. Zion is a painful memory.*

54

4. O how could we sing
   the song of the Lord
   on alien soil?

5. If I forget you, Jerusalem,
   let my right hand wither!
6. O let my tongue
   cleave to my mouth
   if I remember you not,
   if I prize not Jerusalem
   above all my joys!

A curse on me if I should forget Zion — let me have no hand for the harp, no tongue for song!

7. Remember, O Lord,
   against the sons of Edom
   the day of Jerusalem;
   when they said: 'Tear it down!
   Tear it down to its foundations!'
8. O Babylon, destroyer,
   he is happy who repays you
   the ills you brought on us.
9. He shall seize and shall dash
   your children on the rock!

God, too, must remember Zion — and her enemies! The dark side of the singer's love for Jerusalem: deadly hatred for those who would destroy her: Babylon, of course, but perhaps more bitterly, Edom — a neighbour and brother who 'gloated over your brother on the day of his misfortune' (Ob 12)

In the calamity of the exile only the strongest emotions survived — a fierce love for Jerusalem and an equally fierce hatred for her enemies. There was a special vengeance reserved for the people of Edom, to the south of the Salt Sea. They were related to the Israelites, being descendants of Esau the brother of Israel/Jacob. When the Babylonians were destroying Jerusalem it seems the Edomites rejoiced, and even took part in the looting and in rounding up the fleeing survivors; for this they were condemned by the prophet Obadiah:

You should not have entered the gate of my people
  in the day of his calamity;
You should not have gloated over his disaster
  in the day of his calamity;
you should not have looted his goods
  in the day of his calamity.
You should not have stood at the parting of the ways
  to cut off his fugitives;
you should not have delivered up his survivors
  in the day of distress.   (see Obadiah 11-14 *JB*)

Exercise 39:   *Refugees are numbered in millions in our world today — people who have been driven from their homes and land by famine, drought, war or political upheaval. Many are being helped in refugee camps and temporary shelters. What do you think will happen to them if they cannot return to their homes? How can they keep their identity, their sense of who they are? Where can they find hope, and what can we do for them?*

In all the devastation of the Exile in Babylon, the greatest danger to the exiles was the loss of their identity. Land, city, Temple and king — all were gone; in a foreign land they could sing no praise of their God; the Story was ended. They could easily have vanished from history, as so many other uprooted and dispossessed peoples have done. That they survived was due to two factors. The first was the emergence of a new world power to the east of Babylon: Persia, under its king, Cyrus. In 539 BC the Persians defeated the Babylonians and dismantled their empire. The following year, Cyrus issued an edict allowing the captive peoples, among them the Israelites, to return to their countries (see 2 Chronicles 36:17-23; Ezra 1:1-11).

The other factor of vital importance to the survival of Israel was the vision of the prophets, in particular of three men with personal experience of either the destruction of Jerusalem or the exile in Babylon — Jeremiah, Ezekiel, and the anonymous Exile Prophet (whose words are to be found in Isaiah 40-55). Between them, these three rebuilt the identity and the hope of the exiles. For these prophets, the Exile was not the end but the ground of a new beginning. It is typical of God to create the future out of failure, and this the prophets saw him do in Babylon. And so they borrowed from the events of Israel's past and began to speak of new things. They began to tell the Story again.

Jeremiah   had lived through the disintegration of Israel in the decades before the Exile, and had watched despair settle on the people:

> Incurable sorrow overtakes me,
> my heart fails me.
> Hark, from the daughter of my people the cry for help,
> ringing far and wide throughout the land!
> 'Is Yahweh no longer in Zion,
> her King no longer there?'   *Jr 8:18-19*

Now he speaks of a *new Covenant* 'with the House of Israel and the House of Judah, but not like the covenant I made with their ancestors on the day I took them by the hand to bring them out of Egypt, a covenant which they broke. . . Within them I shall plant my Law, writing it on their hearts.' (see Jeremiah 31:31-34). What is astonishing — and heartening for the exiles — is not the newness of this Covenant, nor its emphasis on interior commitment, but the sheer fact that *God still wants a covenant* with Israel. The people should not forget who they are, for God has not forgotten them.

For *Ezekiel* it was a matter of life and death: Israel had been reduced to a pile of dead, dry bones (see Ezekiel 37:1-14). There must be a return to life: 'I shall give you a new heart, and put a new spirit in you; I shall remove the heart of stone from your bodies and give you a heart of flesh instead. . . You will live in the country which I gave to your ancestors. You will be my people and I shall be your God' (*Ezk 36:24-28*). No, the Exile is not the end; they will come back to life, they will again be God's people and will live in their own country.

As we read these prophecies we are amazed at the hopefulness of Jeremiah and Ezekiel. Neither the ruin of Jerusalem nor the deportation of the people could darken their vision — they saw new life, new spirit, new beginnings growing out of the death and despair of the Exile years. It is from the *Exile Prophet* that we most clearly learn the ground of this hope. Yahweh, the Covenant-maker, the life-giver, is also the Creator.

> How can you say, Jacob, how can you repeat, Israel,
> 'My way is hidden from Yahweh,
> my rights are ignored by my God'?
> Did you not know? Had you not heard?
> Yahweh is the everlasting God,
> he created the remotest parts of the earth.
> He does not grow tired or weary,
> his understanding is beyond fathoming.
> He gives strength to the weary,
> He strengthens the powerless.   (see Isaiah 40:21-31)

This alters everything! If Yahweh is the Creator, the Lord of all peoples and lands, then he is master of the Babylonians and the Persians too! And so it is: as the Exile Prophet saw, it is precisely Yahweh who sends Cyrus to free his people:

> Thus says Yahweh to his anointed one,
> to Cyrus whom, he says, I have grasped by his right hand. . . .
> It is for the sake of my servant Jacob
> and of Israel my chosen one,
> that I have called you by your name. . . . (see Isaiah 45:1-7)

From this insight grows all the vision of the Exile prophet — a new exodus, a new city, a new relationship with God, and a renewed identity: they have a *name*:-

> And now, thus says Yahweh,
> he who created you, Jacob,
> who formed you, Israel:
> do not be afraid, for I have redeemed you;
> I have called you by your name, you are mine.   *Is 43:1*

And they can begin to sing again:

Psalm 126   Song for a Homecoming

1. When the Lord delivered Zion from bondage,
   it seemed like a dream.
2. Then was our mouth filled with laughter,
   on our lips there were songs.

   The heathens themselves said: 'What marvels
   the Lord worked for them!'
3. What marvels the Lord worked for us!
   Indeed we were glad.

4. Deliver us, O Lord, from our bondage
   as streams in dry land.
5. Those who are sowing in tears
   will sing when they reap.

6. They go out, they go out, full of tears,
   carrying seed for the sowing:
   they come back, they come back, full of song,
   carrying their sheaves.

The return from exile: a time of laughter and song

A time to build and a time to plant — and we have seen streams in the desert! (see Isaiah 43:16-21)

The return from the Babylonian exile would open a new chapter in Israel's story — and add a new dimension to the *identity of God*: 'Look, the days are coming, Yahweh declares, when people will no longer say, "As Yahweh lives who brought the Israelites out of Egypt!" but, "As Yahweh lives who brought the Israelites back from the land of the north and all the countries to which he had driven them".' (*Jr 16:14-15*)

4 THE WORLD AROUND US

We begin with an exercise:

Exercise 40:   *What stories do you know in your own tradition about the creation of the world? Can you tell some of these stories? In small groups discuss: What is the meaning of these creation stories? Why were they told?*

4.1   IN THE BEGINNING

The Hebrews, and the other peoples who lived around them, had their own traditions about the making of the world. These stories were told and re-told over many hundreds of years, and were passed on from generation to generation. In the end, they were gathered together and written down, and they now form part of the Bible — they are stories of God. The early chapters of the Book of *Genesis* contain some of these traditions.

Exercise 41:   *Genesis 1:1 - 2:4a contains one of the Hebrew traditions about the making of the world in seven days. Please read the scripture text, and for each day write a summary in the space provided in the grid below:*

Genesis 1:1-2	Introduction: 'In the beginning. . . Chaos, darkness, abyss, wind (spirit) over the waters.
Genesis 1:3-4 DAY 1	
Genesis 1:6-8 DAY 2	
Genesis 1:9-13 DAY 3	
Genesis 1:14-19 DAY 4	
Genesis 1:20-23 DAY 5	

58

Genesis 1:24-31 DAY 6	
Genesis 2:1-3 DAY 7	
Genesis 2:4a	Conclusion: 'Such is the story of the heavens and the earth at their creation'.

The account of creation in Genesis 1 must be appreciated for what it is, a poetic, dramatic telling of how God is the world's maker. It does not set out to show the details of the way the world was made — it is not a 'scientific' description, as we would understand that term. In a word, it does not give a *literal* account of creation; it does much more than that — it explores the *meaning of creation*. There need be no clash between the Genesis account and a modern scientific account of creation. A scientist would try to explain what happened in terms of forces, time, space, energy and matter. The Genesis author was celebrating creation, and he wrote a poem.

The world was a cause of much joy for the Hebrews, and they had many songs in praise of its Maker. Some of them (as we have seen in Chapter 1.2 and 1.3) were used in processions during Temple worship:

> The Lord's is the earth and its fullness,
> the world and all its peoples.
> It is he who set it on the seas;
> on the waters he made it firm.　　*Ps 24:1-2*

> In his hand are the depths of the earth;
> the heights of the mountains are his.
> To him belongs the sea, for he made it
> and the dry land shaped by his hands.　　*Ps 95:4-5*

Perhaps the most delightful creation hymn is Psalm 104, which closely follows the story told in Genesis 1.

Exercise 42:　　*Read Psalm 104. Compare the psalm with* Genesis 1, *using your answer to Exercise 41 and writing in the important details in the grid below:*

Genesis	Psalm 104
Genesis 1:3-5 DAY 1	Ps 104:2a　God is 'wrapped in *light* as in a robe'.
Genesis 1:6-8 DAY 2	Ps 104:2b-4
Genesis 1:9-13 DAY 3	Ps 104:5-17
Genesis 1:14-19 DAY 4	Ps 104:19-22
Genesis 1:20-23 DAY 5	Ps 104:25-26 (also vv 12,17 - birds)

Genesis 1:24-31   Ps 104:27-30
   DAY 6
                 (also vv 11,14,18 - animals and humans)

Genesis 2:1-3   Ps 104:31-32   God's majesty, and his delight in his works
   DAY 7

Psalm 104 is a celebration of life — the world teems with living creatures, and 'all of them look to you' (*v 27*). It is the *spirit* or *breath* (the Hebrew word *ruach* can mean 'spirit', 'breath' or 'wind') of God that gives and renews life (*vv 29-30*), and so the psalmist can dedicate his whole life to praising God:

> I will sing to the Lord all my life,
> make music to my God while I live.   *v 33*

The first response of the Hebrew to the fact of creation was to sing God's praises, and to invite all creatures to sing with him. *Psalm 148* contains a sequence of praise that comes to focus on the people of Israel — it is as if the whole of creation were centred on Jerusalem and the Temple and the worship that takes place there:

Psalm 148   The Song of Creation

1. Alleluia!
   Praise the Lord from the heavens,
   praise him in the heights.
2. Praise him, all his angels,
   praise him, all his host.

(Genesis 1:1) *The Hebrews envisaged the heavenly host of angels living above the sky; they are to praise Yahweh.*

3. Praise him, sun and moon,
   praise him, shining stars.
4. Praise him, highest heavens
   and the waters above the heavens.
5. Let them praise the name of the Lord.
   He commanded: they were made.
6. He fixed them for ever,
   gave a law which shall not pass away.

(Genesis 1:3-8,14-19) *The next lower level of creation: sun, moon, stars, and the waters above the sky. God made them by a command, and now they praise the Name.*

7. Praise the Lord from the earth,
   sea creatures and all oceans,
8. fire and hail, snow and mist,
   stormy winds that obey his word;
9. all mountains and hills,
   all fruit trees and cedars,
10. beasts, wild and tame,
    reptiles and birds on the wing;

(Genesis 1:9-13,20-25) *All the elements, wind and rain, hills, trees, animals and birds: praise Yahweh!*

11. all earth's kings and peoples,
    earth's princes and rulers;
12. young men and maidens,
    old men together with children.
13. Let them praise the name of the Lord
    for he alone is exalted.
    The splendour of his name
    reaches beyond heaven and earth.

(Genesis 1:26-31) *Humankind in every land and language join to praise the Name.*

60

14. He exalts the strength of his people.
    He is the praise of all his saints,
    of the sons of Israel,
    of the people to whom he comes close.
    Alleluia!

> *Mention of the Name brings this song within the story of Israel, 'of the people to whom he comes close.' The God of Moses is the Creator!*

Exercise 43:   *Genesis 1, Psalm 104 and Psalm 148 all regard creation through the language of poetry. Could you express one of these poems through a different language — mime, or drama, or drawing, or on a video?*

4.2 WATER-TALK

Read the following passages:

> The waves of death rose about me;
> the torrents of destruction assailed me;
> the snares of the grave entangled me;
> the traps of death confronted me.   *Ps 18:5-6*

> You have laid me in the depths of the tomb,
> in the places that are dark, in the depths.
> Your anger weighs down upon me:
> I am drowned beneath your waves.   *Ps 88:7-8*

> Save me, O God,
> for the waters have risen to my neck.
> I have sunk into the mud of the deep
> and there is no foothold.
> I have entered the waters of the deep
> and the waves overwhelm me.   *Ps 69:2-3*

In each of these psalms the singer is in great anguish — he sees himself being overwhelmed in a sea of troubles. He is surrounded by enemies, or caught by some dread disease, some awful fear, even the anger of God. Whatever it is that threatens him, it could very well destroy him utterly. In such an extreme, he reaches for the strongest language available to him: the language of the Exodus. The incident at the Red Sea gave rise to a way of speaking about God:

> He threatened the Red Sea; it dried up
> and he led them through the deep as through the desert.   *Ps 106:9*

Surely he can do as much for the psalmist: 'reach down from heaven and save me; draw me out of the mighty waters' (*Ps 144:7*). The singer uses the image of mighty waters to describe the awful forces that could crush his life, were it not for the greater power of God to save him.

However, the roots of this water-talk go back even further than the Exodus, for at the Creation, too, God divided and tamed the waters:

> God said, 'Let there be a vault through the middle of the waters to divide the waters in two.' And so it was. God made the vault, and it divided the waters under the vault from the waters above the vault. God called the vault 'heaven'. Evening came and morning came: the second day. God said, 'Let the waters under heaven come together into a single mass, and let dry land appear.' And so it was. God called the dry land 'earth' and the mass of waters 'seas', and God saw that it was good.   *Gn 1:6-10*

As Genesis 1 saw it, before God created our world, 'the earth was a formless void, there was darkness over the deep, with a divine wind sweeping over the waters'. (*1:2*) It was these waters of chaos that God divided and controlled in the story of creation. Perhaps a picture of the world as the Hebrews imagined it will help us to understand what they saw God as doing.

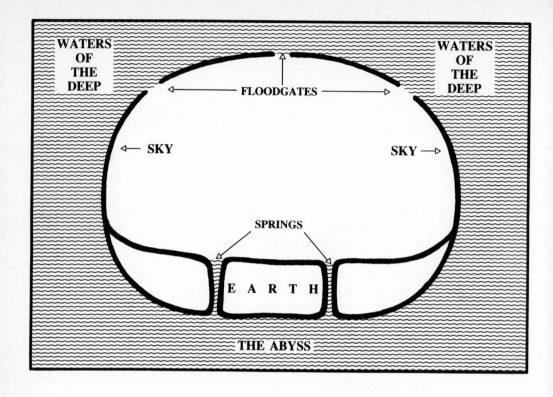

By making a 'sky' to separate the waters of chaos, God created a kind of bubble in the waters of the deep — our world! We live, then, surrounded by the Great Waters in a space held open by the constant providence of God. It is his power alone that keeps the waters from rushing together again and destroying all creation — just as it was his power that kept the waters of the Red Sea open in the Exodus. Later in the book of Genesis, the story of the Great Flood contains a description of the imminent breakdown of our world, when 'all the springs of the great deep burst through, and the sluices of heaven opened' (*Gn 7:11*). The bubble was about to burst! The springs of water in the earth, and the openings in the sky that allowed rain to fall, were about to crack open wide so that the 'great deep' would smother the world again.

Exercise 44: *Discuss this Hebrew understanding of the world. Compare it with a modern, scientific description of the earth — remembering that the Hebrew image was based on the best 'science' of their time, more than 3,000 years ago. Do we have anything to learn from this ancient image of the universe?*

Exodus and Creation are both described in terms of God's supreme mastery over water-force; this power of God was celebrated in the Psalms:

Psalm 93 'Who is this, that even the wind and the sea obey him?'

1. The Lord is king, with majesty enrobed; ⎤ *Proclamation and intro-*
   the Lord has robed himself with might,   ⎥ *duction to the prayer that*
   he has girded himself with power.   ⎦ *follows*

The world you made firm, not to be moved;
2. your throne has stood firm from of old.
   From all eternity, O Lord, you are.
3. The waters have lifted up, O Lord,
   the waters have lifted up their voice,
   the waters have lifted up their thunder.
4. Greater than the roar of mighty waters,
   more glorious than the surgings of the sea,
   the Lord is glorious on high.
5. Truly your decrees are to be trusted.
   Holiness is fitting to your house,
   O Lord, until the end of time.

God is in his heavenly palace, and his home is in the Temple too. He is more powerful than the waters — whether of Exodus or of Creation. And his Law lasts for ever

For the Hebrews, the sea always held a certain dread. Though they lived on the eastern shores of the Mediterranean, they never became a seafaring nation. And in Psalm 107, where the pattern of God's pity is explored in a series of dangers, the last and most elaborately described is a storm at sea (see Chapter 2.4):-

Some sailed to the sea in ships
to trade on the mighty waters.
These men have seen the Lord's deeds,
the wonders he does in the deep.
For he spoke; he summoned the gale,
tossing the waves of the sea
up to heaven and back into the deep;
their soul melted away in their distress.
They staggered, reeled like drunken men,
for all their skill was gone.
Then they cried to the Lord in their need
and he rescued them from their distress.   *Ps 107:23-28*

Even the storm at sea is under God's control — it is he who 'summoned the gale'! In Jesus' time, the same fear of raging waters persisted. When he calmed a violent storm (the word used literally means an earthquake!) on the Sea of Galilee, the disciples asked, 'Whatever kind of man is this, that even the winds and the sea obey him?' (see Matthew 8:23-27). And in his vision of a renewed world in *Revelation*, the author writes:

Then I saw a new heaven and a new earth; the first heaven and the first earth had disappeared now, and *there was no longer any sea.*   *21:1*

The ultimate threat had been removed: if there were no more sea, there was no more danger of the world being overwhelmed by the waters of chaos.

Exercise 45:   *Here are some more examples of water-talk in the Psalms:*

Psalm 69:15-16
Psalm 77:17-21
Psalm 78:12-13
Psalm 104:5-9
Psalm 144:7

Some of these examples refer directly to Exodus or Creation; others use water language to describe situations of need or anguish in the life of the psalmist.

Whatever the case, it is the Lord who opens a path for us through the waters, to bring us to life and to freedom. Do you think this water-talk could contribute to our understanding of Baptism, and in what way?

4.3 THE MAKER AND THE SAVIOUR

Psalm 136, the Great Hallel (sung during the Passover Meal) celebrates the love of God for us. The refrain, repeated after each line as in a litany, proclaims that God's *hesed* endures for ever. *Hesed* is a Hebrew word, translated variously, 'love' (*Grail, Jerusalem Bible, New English Bible*), or 'mercy' (*New American Bible, King James Version*), or 'steadfast love' (*Revised Standard Version*), or 'faithful love' (*New Jerusalem Bible*). It means, in a word, all that God is and does for us; Psalm 136 spells out God's many ways of loving us.

Exercise 46:   *Read Psalm 136.*

vv 1-3   A call to thanksgiving. *'God of gods', 'Lord of Lords' is a Hebrew way of saying, the Greatest God, the mightiest Lord.*

vv 4-9   Creation: *skies, seas, sun, moon, stars — as in Genesis 1:6-19*

vv 10-15   Exodus: *death of first-born, Red Sea crossing, defeat of Pharaoh (Exodus 12:29 - 14:31)*

vv 16-22   Desert wandering: *defeat of all enemies, entry to Promised Land (Numbers 11-14; Joshua 1-4)*

vv 23-26   God remembers us, *and all creation. He is God of heaven — and he loves us!*

Psalm 136 tells the Story, but beginning with creation. Can you continue the Psalm with reference to your own life — in what ways has God shown you that 'his love endures for ever'?

We have looked at the story of the People of Israel, that is, their *salvation history* (all that God has done for them in helping and protecting them and in giving them a land to live in, but especially in making them his own people). The people rejoiced in the God who saved them, and even as they did so they began to realise an even deeper truth: the God who led Israel through the Red Sea is in fact the same and only God who made the whole world. It is not just that Yahweh had made them his own people, but that he had *made them*. We take this for granted, but in an earlier age it was something the People had to come to realise. Their story is also the story of one people's search for the *One* God, that there is only *One* — and that One has shared his Name with them. And if only One, then all works of Making and Saving are his. This is the message and the joy of Psalm 136.

The same single vision of God the Creator and Saviour is found in *Psalm 147*. The story of Salvation, particularly in the rebuilding of Jerusalem after the Babylonian exile, and the story of Creation mingle easily in this great song of praise. (There may in fact be three distinct hymns joined in this psalm — notice the repeated calls to praise God in vv 1, 7 and 12.)

Psalm 147 (146 & 147 in Grail)   Praise the Maker and Saviour

(I)
Leader:

1. Praise the Lord for he is good;
   sing to our God for he is loving:
   to him our praise is due.   *Call to praise*

'Salvation Choir'

2. The Lord builds up Jerusalem
   and brings back Israel's exiles,   *The return from exile,
   comforting the afflicted (see*
3. he heals the broken-hearted,   *Isaiah 40:1-2)*
   he binds up all their wounds.

'Creation Choir'
    4. He fixes the number of the stars;
       he calls each one by its name.

       Making and naming the stars (Isaiah 40:25-26)

All:
5. Our Lord is great and almighty;
   his wisdom can never be measured.
6. The Lord raises the lowly;
   he humbles the wicked to the dust.

       God loves the lowly.

(II)
Leader:
7. O sing to the Lord, giving thanks;
   sing psalms to our God with the harp.

       Call to praise

'Creation Choir'
    8. He covers the heavens with clouds;
       he prepares the rain for the earth,
       making mountains sprout with grass
       and with plants to serve man's needs.
    9. He provides the beasts with their food
       and young ravens that call upon him.

       God sends life (see Isaiah 41:17-20; 44:1-4).

All:
10. His delight is not in horses
    nor his pleasure in warrior's strength.
11. The Lord delights in those who revere him,
    in those who wait for his love.

       God loves the loving

(III)
Leader:
12. O praise the Lord, Jerusalem!
    Zion, praise your God!

       Call to praise — to Jerusalem!

'Salvation Choir'
    13. He has strengthened the bars of your gates,
       he has blessed the children within you.
    14. He established peace on your borders,
       be feeds you with finest wheat.

       Rebuilding the City (see Isaiah 52:7-9)

'Creation Choir'
    15. He sends out his word to the earth
       and swiftly runs his command.
    16. He showers down snow white as wool,
       he scatters hoar-frost like ashes.
    17. He hurls down hailstones like crumbs.
       The waters are frozen at his touch;
    18. he sends forth his word and it melts them:
       at the breath of his mouth the waters flow.

       Making with a word: (see Genesis 1; Isaiah 55:10-11)

All:
19. He makes his word known to Jacob,
    to Israel his laws and decrees.
20. He has not dealt thus with other nations;
    he has not taught them his decrees.
    Alleluia!

       God loves Israel.

Exercise 47:   *Along the left margin of Psalm 147 as reproduced above, you will find suggestions as to who might sing different parts of the psalm: 'Leader', 'Creation Choir', 'Salvation Choir'. This is not a reconstruction of the way the psalm could have been sung in the Temple, but it is a way in which we might pray the psalm. Can you experiment a little to discover if this might be a helpful way for you to pray this psalm?*
How do you think the 'creation' sections and the 'salvation' sections might apply to your life?

In Psalm 147 there is no sharp distinction between God's *creative* attitude and his *saving* attitude — what he does in making the world and what he does for his people and for Jerusalem. The God who led Israel through the Red Sea is the same God who made the whole world. He is more powerful than Israel had ever imagined.

> Who was it measured the water of the sea
>   in the hollow of his hand
> and calculated the heavens to the nearest inch,
> gauged the dust of the earth to the nearest bushel,
> weighed the mountains in scales,
> the hills in a balance?

> He who sits enthroned above the circle of the earth,
> the inhabitants of which are like grasshoppers,
> stretches out the heavens like a cloth,
> spreads them out like a tent to live in.   *Is 40:12,22*

It was during the time of the exile in Babylon that this insight into the greatness of God had its strongest expression. It was the foundation for the teaching of the Exile Prophet (whose words are to be found in the Book of Isaiah 40-55). At a time of despair for the exiles who feared they had lost their Temple, their City, their Land — and perhaps even their God — the prophet speaks to them:

> And now, thus says Yahweh,
> he who created you, Jacob,
> who formed you, Israel:
> Do not be afraid, for I have redeemed you;
> I have called you by your name, you are mine.
> Should you pass through the waters, I shall be with you;
> or through rivers, they will not swallow you up.

> To the north I shall say, 'Give them up!'
> and to the south, 'Do not hold them back!'
> Bring back my sons from far away
> and my daughters from the remotest part of the earth,
> everyone who bears my name,
> whom I have created for my glory,
> whom I have formed, whom I have made.   *Is 43:1-2,6-7*

They had not known their God was so great! This is a God of life!

Psalm 115 celebrates this God of life, and calls for trust in him by mocking other 'gods' and those who worship them. For Israel, it could never be a matter of choosing between several possible gods, but of recognising the One God. It is the difference between worshipping the Creator or one of his creatures. Psalm 115 is a drama, a kind of 'benediction service', in which the people are led to receive the blessing of God through his priest (vv 14-15). And this blessing is *life* — something the dead idols cannot give. But for the Hebrews, to live is to praise — so the service ends with a final hymn of praise — the response of the people to the blessing of life.

Psalm 115   A Benediction Service

All:

1. Not to us, Lord, not to us,
   but to your name give the glory
   for the sake of your love and your truth,
2. lest the heathen say: 'Where is their God?'
3. But our God is in the heavens;
   he does whatever he wills.

Opening song: may God's name be known to all.

Choir:

4. Their idols are silver and gold,
   the work of human hands.
5. They have mouths but they cannot speak;
   they have eyes but they cannot see;
6. they have ears but they cannot hear;
   they have nostrils but they cannot smell.
7. With their hands they cannot feel;
   with their feet they cannot walk.
   No sound comes from their throats.
8. Their makers will come to be like them
   and so will all who trust in them.

The Lord and the idols: they can do nothing — 'he does whatever he wills'. You become like the god you trust (vv 8-11).

Leader and People:

9. Sons of Israel, trust in the Lord.
   ℞ He is their help and their shield.
10. Sons of Aaron, trust in the Lord.
    ℞ He is their help and their shield.
11. You who fear him, trust in the Lord.
    ℞ He is their help and their shield.

See similar groupings in Pss 118:2-4; 135:19-20. The third group, 'you who fear him', may refer to proselytes.

All:

12. He remembers us, and he will bless us;
    he will bless the sons of Israel.
    He will bless the sons of Aaron.
13. The Lord will bless those who fear him,
    the little no less than the great.

Priest:

14. To you may the Lord grant increase,
    to you and all your children.
15. May you be blessed by the Lord,
    the maker of heaven and earth.

BLESSING from the Creator: life, increase, children

All:

16. The heavens belong to the Lord
    but the earth he has given to men.
17. The dead shall not praise the Lord,
    nor those who go down into the silence.
18. But we who live bless the Lord
    now and for ever. Amen.

Final hymn of praise from the living — a response to the blessing of life

Exercise 48:   *Enact Psalm 115 — if possible, with a dramatisation of vv 4-8. What kinds of 'idols' might we construct for ourselves today? In what way might we 'come to be like them'? How might we become like God?*

4.4 CREATION AND FORGIVENESS

The work of creation, according to Genesis I, reached a climax in the making of humankind: 'God said, ''Let us make man in our own image, in the likeness of ourselves, and let them be masters of the fish of the sea, the birds of heaven, the cattle, all the wild animals and all the creatures that creep along the ground.''

> God created man in the image of himself,
> in the image of God he created him,
> male and female he created them.'   *Gn 1:26-27*

This making of God's image on the earth is the subject of another story in the second chapter of Genesis:

> At the time when Yahweh God made earth and heaven there was as yet no wild bush on the earth nor had any wild plant yet sprung up, for Yahweh God had not sent rain on the earth, nor was there any man to till the soil. Instead, water flowed out of the ground and watered all the surface of the soil.
>
> Yahweh God shaped man from the soil of the ground and blew the breath of life into his nostrils, and man became a living being. Yahweh God planted a garden in Eden, which is in the east, and there he put the man he had fashioned.
>
> Yahweh God said, 'It is not right that the man should be alone. I shall make him a helper.' So from the soil Yahweh God fashioned all the wild animals and all the birds of heaven. These he brought to the man to see what he would call them; each one was to bear the name the man would give it. The man gave names to all the cattle, all the birds of heaven and all the wild animals. But no helper suitable for the man was found for him.
>
> Then, Yahweh God made the man fall into a deep sleep. And, while he was asleep, he took one of his ribs and closed the flesh up again forthwith. Yahweh God fashioned the rib he had taken from the man into a woman, and brought her to the man. And the man said:
>> This one at last is bone of my bones
>> and flesh of my flesh!
>> She is to be called Woman,
>> because she was taken from Man.
>
> This is why a man leaves his father and mother and becomes attached to his wife, and they become one flesh.   *Gn 2:4b-8,18-24*

Exercise 49:   *Read the above passage from Genesis 2. Note the following:*

    (a) The man 'adam' is made from the soil 'adamah'. Soil (ground, clay) is important in this story. In the beginning, a desert land which God waters to make a garden. The man and, later, the animals are made from the same ground.

    (b) God moulds the man as a potter might do: God touches the man intimately, fingers in the clay.

    (c) Life for the man comes from the breath blown into his nostrils by God — the moving air a sign of the spirit (ruach).

    (d) The woman is not made directly from the ground, but is of the same flesh with man: woman, ishshah, is taken from man, ish. A unique unity between man and woman.

    (e) God made the man and the woman equal: the man gives names to the animals (a sign of his power over them) but he does not — as yet —

name the woman. *(But see Genesis 3:20, after the 'Fall', when the man does name her. What is the significance of that?)*

(f) *The creation of the world, and of the image of God on the earth, is complete only with the making of woman. (see Genesis 1:27)*

This story in Genesis 2 need not be taken literally; it is a dramatic expression of the meaning of humankind and our place in the world as the writer saw it. Perhaps the best way to appreciate it is by drama and mime. Let the group read and discuss the story, and how they might dramatise it. After the drama, discuss the story again — has the drama helped you to understand it?

These stories of creation give rise to a great sense of wonder at the world, a delight in the love of God for us. The world is full of mysteries, not least the mystery of ourselves: who are we? Psalm 8 is one singer's response to the wonder of the world.

Psalm 8 The psalmist's 'Magnificat'

People:

2. How great is your name, O Lord our God,
   through all the earth!

   Response: *praising the NAME!*

Singer:

Your majesty is praised above the heavens;
3. on the lips of children and of babes
   you have found praise to foil the enemy,
   to silence the foe and the rebel.
4. When I see the heavens, the work of your hands,
   the moon and the stars which you arranged,
5. what is man that you should keep him in mind,
   mortal man that you should care for him?

The same teaching as Genesis 1 and 2 — we are only children, given care of the stars! What a mystery lies in us!

6. Yet you have made him little less than a god;
   with glory and honour you crowned him,
7. gave him power over the works of your hand,
   put all things under his feet.
8. All of them, sheep and cattle,
   yes, even the savage beasts,
9. birds of the air, and fish
   that make their way through the waters.

People:

10. How great is your name, O Lord our God,
    through all the earth!

    Response: *the NAME, the source of our mystery*

Exercise 50:   *Small-group discussions:*

1. *What is man that you should keep him in mind, mortal man that you care for him?*
   The psalmist asks a question; perhaps you might try to give your own answer.

2. *(You) gave him power over the works of your hand, put all things under his feet.*
   What kind of 'power' over creation has God given to us? What does this mean for the way we use the things of the earth? Are we responsible for the world?

All these stories and psalms of the creation are really love-stories — God made us because he loved us. It was true of the Exodus: God chose and saved his people 'because he loved you and meant to keep the oath which he swore to your ancestors' (see Deuteronomy 7:7ff). And it is true of creation too — it is as if, even before we were made, God knew us and heard our cry to be created, and he could not bear to leave us unmade. We belong to the 'plans of his heart from age to age', as Psalm 33 describes it.

Psalm 33 Creation and the faithful love of God

1. Ring out your joy to the Lord, O you just;
   for praise is fitting for loyal hearts.
2. Give thanks to the Lord upon the harp,
   with a ten-stringed lute sing him songs.
3. O sing him a song that is new,
   play loudly, with all your skill.
4. For the word of the Lord is faithful
   and all his works to be trusted.
5. The Lord loves justice and right
   and fills the earth with his love.

A LEADER calls for a new song! God's word and work share the same qualities; they are constant, consistent, just, loving. His word is made tangible in his work — creation is his love touching us.

6. By his word the heavens were made,
   by the breath of his mouth all the stars.
7. He collects the waves of the ocean;
   he stores up the depths of the sea.
8. Let all the earth fear the Lord,
   all who live in the world revere him.
9. He spoke; and it came to be.
   He commanded; it sprang into being.

THE NEW SONG
(vv 6-19) *6-9 Genesis-talk: in Hebrew,* dabar *means both word and deed. What God says — is! We live within his spoken word.*

10. He frustrates the designs of the nations,
    he defeats the plans of the peoples.
11. His own designs shall stand for ever,
    the plans of his heart from age to age.

10-11 The heart of the matter: God has a desire for us, he plans a life for us.

12. They are happy, whose God is the Lord,
    the people he has chosen as his own.
13. From the heavens the Lord looks forth,
    he sees all the children of men.
14. From the place where he dwells he gazes
    on all the dwellers on the earth,
15. he who shapes the hearts of them all
    and considers all their deeds.
16. A king is not saved by his army,
    nor a warrior preserved by his strength.
17. A vain hope for safety is the horse;
    despite its power it cannot save.
18. The Lord looks on those who revere him,
    on those who hope in his love,
19. to rescue their souls from death,
    to keep them alive in famine.

12-19 The Story: God chooses us, guards us, judges us, watches over us — because of his hesed, *his faithful love.*

20. Our soul is waiting for the Lord.
    The Lord is our help and our shield.
21. In him do our hearts find joy.
    We trust in his holy name.
22. May your love be upon us, O Lord,
    as we place all our hope in you.

RESPONSE OF THE PEOPLE: *God is worth waiting for, because of his faithful love.*

70

Creation is an act of forgiveness. The creation songs and stories teach us that the 'whole earth' is a sign of God's faithful love for us. Before we were made, before anything we had done for good or evil, God had already accepted and loved us. He had forgiven us before we even had need for forgiveness. He knew our weakness — and he loved us still, as the writer of Psalm 139 knew well:

13. For it was you who created my being,
knit me together in my mother's womb.
14. I thank you for the wonder of my being,
for the wonders of all your creation.
Already you knew my soul,
15. my body held no secret from you
when I was being fashioned in secret
and moulded in the depths of the earth.
16. Your eyes saw all my actions,
they were all of them written in your book;
every one of my days was decreed
before one of them came into being.

But if to create is to forgive, so too is forgiveness an act of creation. When God forgives us, he renews us, gives us life again, puts a new spirit (breath) into us, as he did at the Creation (Genesis 2:7). Ezekiel's vision of the dead, dry bones was an experience of God's forgiveness for 'the whole House of Israel. They keep saying, "Our bones are dry, our hope has gone; we are done for." So, prophesy. Say to them, "The Lord Yahweh says this: I am now going to open your graves. . . and put my spirit in you".' (see Ezekiel 36:25-27; 37:1-14) The psalmist, too, knows the same rushing Spirit/breath of God, the same re-creation in his sinfulness:

10. Make me hear rejoicing and gladness,
that the bones you have crushed may thrill.
11. From my sins turn away your face
and blot out all my guilt.
12. A pure heart create for me, O God,
put a steadfast spirit within me.
13. Do not cast me away from your presence,
nor deprive me of your holy spirit.
14. Give me again the joy of your help;
with a spirit of fervour sustain me.   *Ps 51*

Three times he calls for a new spirit (new breath, new life). Even more dramatically, he asks God to *create for him* (v 12) — the Hebrew word *bara*, used only of God, and found in Genesis 1:1 ('In the beginning God created heaven and earth.') It is also found in the prophets who speak of a new life for Israel after the disaster of the Babylonian exile: Isaiah 65:17 ('For look, I am going to create new heavens and a new earth.'), Jeremiah 31:22 ('For Yahweh is creating something new on earth. . .'). They say, 'to err is human, to forgive divine' because forgiveness is like an act of creation.

Exercise 51:   Group discussion: *When God forgives, it can be like an act of creation, he makes us new. When we forgive, do you think we too can make someone new? If we refuse to forgive someone, are we in fact blocking that person from growing, from becoming? Have you ever been refused forgiveness, did anyone ever refuse to be reconciled with you? How did you feel about that?*

Psalm 32 The Song of the Prodigal Son

1. Happy the man whose offence is forgiven,
   whose sin is remitted.
2. O happy the man to whom the Lord
   imputes no guilt,
   in whose spirit is no guile.

   The singer introduces the theme: forgiveness brings blessing.

3. I kept it secret and my frame was wasted.
   I groaned all day long
4. for night and day your hand
   was heavy upon me.
   Indeed my strength was dried up
   as by the summer's heat.
5. But now I have acknowledged my sins;
   my guilt I did not hide.
   I said: 'I will confess
   my offence to the Lord.'
   And you, Lord, have forgiven
   the guilt of my sin.

   The experience of the singer expressed in a prayer to God. So long as he refused to admit his guilt and need he was subject to wasting and death. Confessing his sin brought immediate healing and forgiveness.

6. So let every good man pray to you
   in the time of need.
   The floods of water may reach high
   but him they shall not reach.
7. You are my hiding place, O Lord;
   you save me from distress.
   You surround me with cries of deliverance.

   Song of thanksgiving and trust: whoever hides in God will be safe from the deadly waters.

8. I will instruct you and teach you
   the way you should go;
   I will give you counsel
   with my eye upon you:
9. 'Be not like horse and mule, unintelligent,
   needing bridle and bit,
   else they will not approach you.
10. Many sorrows has the wicked
    but he who trusts in the Lord,
    loving mercy surrounds him.'

   A teaching to the community, based on the singer's experience. (Some suggest these verses could be a reply from God to the singer himself. In either case, the lesson is the same.)

   hesed

11. Rejoice, rejoice in the Lord,
    exult, you just!
    O come, ring out your joy,
    all you upright of heart.

   Final song of joy, possibly a response by the people to all they have heard and seen

Exercise 52: Compare Psalm 32 *with the story of the Prodigal Son as told in* Luke 15:11-32. *Note especially:-*

	Psalm 32
— *The sin and suffering of the younger son*	vv 3-4
— *His decision to go to his father and admit his guilt*	v 5a
— *Reaction of the father to his son's return*	v 5b
— *Rejoicing at his safe return*	vv 6-7
— *The father's words to the elder son*	vv 8-10

> — Celebrate and rejoice, 'because your brother here | v 11
> was dead and has come to life; he was lost
> and is found'.
>
> What do the song and the story say to us for our lives? |

4.5 SPACE TO LIVE

So far in this chapter we have been looking at the way the Bible and, in particular, the Psalms speak about Creation. We have seen that in many ways what we distinguish as 'Creation' and 'Salvation' are very similar. It is the same God who is acting in love for his people. Thus, God is described as creating the world and as saving his people from slavery in Egypt in similar ways — by controlling raging waters. The Story of Israel (which is our story too) began not with Moses or Abraham, but with Creation itself. It is all evidence of the *hesed*, the faithful love of God. This means that 'Creation' has a *saving quality* (It is 'for us') and 'Salvation' has a *creative quality (When God saves us, we are made new — a new life, a new spirit, a new people)*. In this section we will see another image of God's approach to us that is both creative and salvific.

The Bible narrative pictures God dividing the waters of the Red Sea to allow the Israelites to escape from Egypt. In other words, he opened a space for them in the waters, a space that meant life for them, just as the closing of that space meant death for the army of Pharaoh. But this space within the Red Sea waters was only a prelude to the space God eventually gave to the Israelites, for after leading them through the desert for forty years, in the end he gave them the land of Canaan.

> Every place you tread with the soles of your feet I shall give you, as I declared to Moses that I would. From the desert and the Lebanon, to the Great River, the Euphrates (the entire country of the Hittites), and as far as the Great Sea to westward, is to be your territory.
> *Jos 1:3-4*

It is a powerful image of the way God saved his people from slavery, that he gave them space, room to grow, open country in which to spread themselves. The image is carried on by the psalms as they describe how God saves his people from any kind of distress. When the singer was surrounded by 'enemies whose strength I could not match':

> He brought me *forth into freedom*,
> he saved me because he loved me.   *Ps 18:20*
>
> In my distress you have *set me at large*   *Ps 4:1 (NJB)*

The literal meaning of the word translated 'distress' or 'anguish' is, to be crushed, oppressed, besieged. To be saved is to be set free from all such oppression.

The same space-making gesture is seen in the Genesis 1 account of Creation. When he divided the waters of chaos, God made room for the world. He gave us space to be. Psalm 104 compares the sky to a tent-cloth: 'You stretch out the heavens like a tent' (*v* 2), and the Exile Prophet takes up the image:

> (God) stretches out the heavens like a cloth,
> spreads them out like a tent to live in.   *Is 40:22*

A tent is a living-space too! So in this way of speaking, the first movement in Creation and in Salvation is to make space, to set free. The psalms which speak of God's pity tell how we are set free from all that threatens to crush us. Psalm 31 is a typical example:

Psalm 31 'Father, into your hands I commit my spirit.' *Lk 23:46*

2. In you, O Lord, I take refuge.
   Let me never be put to shame.
   In your justice, *set me free*,
3. hear me and speedily *rescue me*.
   Be a rock of refuge for me,
   a mighty stronghold to *save me*,
4. for you are my rock, my stronghold.
   For your name's sake, lead me and guide me.
5. *Release* me from the snares they have hidden
   for you are my refuge, Lord.

CRY OF DISTRESS — *set me free, rescue me, save me, release me — for I am falling into their trap.*

6. Into your hands I commend my spirit.
   It is you who will redeem me, Lord.
7. O God of truth, you detest
   those who worship false and empty gods.
8. As for me, I trust in the Lord.

TRUSTING IN THE LORD — *means committing oneself utterly to the living God, rejecting dead idols. (The Hebrew has 'I detest' in v 7.)*

Let me be glad and rejoice in your love.
You who have seen my affliction
and taken heed of my soul's *distress*,
9. have not handed me over to the enemy,
   but *set my feet at large.*

PRAISING THE LORD *who has released me from oppression, and 'set my feet in a broad place' (RSV)*

The rest of Psalm 31 repeats this three-fold pattern on a larger scale:

vv 10-14   cry of distress
vv 15-19   trusting in the Lord
vv 20-23   praising the Lord
vv 24-25   final call to all to join in praise and hope

Behind Psalm 31 lies the image of God opening a space for those who are oppressed or confined in any way. But this calls for an extraordinary trust in God. The Israelites, trapped between the Egyptian army on the one side and the deep Red Sea on the other, were called on to trust God completely: Moses told them 'Have no fear! Stand firm, and you will see what Yahweh will do to save you today: the Egyptians you see today, you will never see again. Yahweh will do the fighting for you: you have only to keep still'. (*Ex 14:13-14 (JB)*) Trust is not a point of arrival, a tranquil, safe haven. It is often blind, tentative, contrite — and always difficult. Trust is being open to the future (the open space), even to the hope that there *is* a future.

Exercise 53:   *Let the group see a photograph or poster of someone who is confined in some way (in prison, in hospital, cowering in fear, in the middle of a hostile crowd. . .) Encourage a discussion, using such questions as:*

What do you see happening?

Can you imagine what it feels like?

How is this person affected by this situation?

How would you help such a person?

If you could help such a person, what change could it make in her/him?

Could you act out what happens to a person who is confined and then set free?

Has such a thing ever happened to you?

There is a great joy and dignity in freedom, but also a great responsibility. One can be set free, be given space, but one is left with the task of using that space rightly. What happens when people are given space can be seen in the story of Israel. After the People had safely crossed the Red Sea from their slavery in Egypt, they were faced with the journey to Mount Sinai and beyond that, to the Land they had been promised. It was a difficult journey, through a wilderness of hunger, thirst and uncertainty. It was a challenge, and it seems the years of slavery had left them with little will for making their own decisions. But they were free now; and they had to *choose* to go to Mount Sinai, to meet God there and to make the Great Choice: 'Moses went and told the people all Yahweh's words and all the laws, and all the people answered with one voice, "All the words Yahweh has spoken we will carry out!" ' (Exodus 24:3). They were no longer slaves; now they could — and must — choose for themselves. This was the greater part of their salvation: they had been led from distress to meet God, and were enabled to choose him who had already chosen them.

The Creation is also a story of choices. That is the meaning of the space-making gesture of God in giving us room in which to live. We are given freedom to choose. The choices made by Adam and Eve, Cain and Abel, Noah and his family, and all the decisions taken by every human being to this day are possible because God has given us freedom to choose.

> He himself made human beings in the beginning,
>   and then left them free to make their own decisions.
> If you choose, you will keep the commandments
>   and so be faithful to his will.   *S 15:14-15*

There are many things that tend to reduce our freedom, to narrow the space given to us: fear, sickness, sin, oppression, ignorance. . . . All of these are a kind of *uncreation*: they diminish us, threaten to crush us, afflict us with anguish. Only the creative, space-making power of God can deliver us from such crushing terrors.

When we talk of space to grow and freedom to choose, we cannot mean only *human* choice. In the *Genesis* imagery, God opened a space in the waters; that is to say, he made room for our world to develop: trees grew in Eden, animals and plants increased and multiplied across the face of the earth, herdsmen and farmers tamed animals and the soil; there was a beginning of metal-working and of music-making, of art, culture, science, society, history, civilisation. And long before that, in the vast reaches of the cosmos, the Universe was growing. God did not make a completed, static world, but a dynamic creation capable of developing and changing in ways we cannot even imagine.

Present-day science would express this in terms of the formation and building of atoms and molecules, of the growth of the stars, of the evolution of life-forms. The beginnings of the universe as we know it lie 15-20 thousand million years ago, the beginnings of life on our planet perhaps 500 million years ago, and humankind is less than 1,000,000 years old. Such is the span of the work of creation — as far as we know! In the space God made for it, creation too was making choices, developing and growing in uncountable numbers of shapes, forms and patterns. The world has its own laws and ways, and we have hardly begun to understand them.

Sometimes creation's changes seem to run counter to life and hope: famine and flood, volcano and earthquake, disease and disfigurement, breakdown of body or mind — there can be a great cruelty in the world. And for all living creatures there is death, whether peacefully or in violence, whether with dignity or shame. All this is part of a creation in which there is room for growth and choice.

Exercise 54:

What does all this tell us about God? What kind of a God would give us such freedom, freedom that would allow such pain in the universe?
Reflect on some of the following passages:-

1. *Referring to the time of exile in Babylon, and God's promise for the future:*

I did forsake you for a brief moment,
but in great compassion I shall take you back.
In a flood of anger, for a moment
I hid my face from you.
But in everlasting love I have taken pity on you,
says Yahweh, your redeemer.   Is 54:7-8

2. From the time before the destruction of Samaria and the Northern Kingdom of Israel
    — God grieves over their unfaithfulness:

I myself taught Ephraim to walk,
I myself took him by the arm,
but they did not know that I was the one caring for them,
that I was leading them with human ties,
with leading strings of love,
that with them, I was like someone lifting an infant to his cheek,
and that I bent down to feed him.   Ho 11:3-4

3. Jesus comes to Jerusalem:

As he drew near and came in sight of the city he shed tears over it and said, 'If you
too had only recognised on this day the way to peace! But in fact it is hidden from
your eyes! Yes, a time is coming when your enemies will raise fortifications all round
you, when they will encircle you and hem you in on every side; they will dash you
and the children inside your walls to the ground; they will leave not one stone standing
on another within you, because you did not recognise the moment of your
visitation.'   Lk 19:41-44

4.6 NEW CREATION

Space-making is an image of creation. It says that to create is to give room for growth, development, choice. God did not make the world in a finished state — the process continues. It is the difference between the making of a motor-car and the making of a child: the one is a finished product, the other only a beginning.

The Psalms tell of the beginning but they do not speak of the end of Creation — that did not fall within the vision of Israel. To find the full meaning of the world and what it was destined to become we have to turn to newer songs, songs in the New Testament writings that expand the horizons of our vision, giving new revelations on both the beginning and the end of Creation. The radical difference between the old songs and the new lies in the latter's vision of Christ as the centre of all creation, the Alpha and the Omega, the beginning and the end.

The Song of the Word (John 1:1-18)
The Song of the Word forms a prologue to the Gospel according to St John. It tells of the Word of God, and the Word's involvement in creation. God made the world by speaking, as we have seen in Genesis 1 and in the Psalms:

> By his word the heavens were made,
> by the breath of his mouth all the stars.   *Ps 33:6 (see Sirach 42:15)*

In Hebrew language and thought, *dabar* means both word and deed, saying and accomplishing. And perhaps the Word of God meant *being* too. This is the thought behind the Song of the Word — that the Word of God has being, and can be spoken of as a person. The Song can be seen as a drama in which the identity of the Word is revealed: one sequence (vv 1-5, 9-14) celebrates how the Word was involved in making the world, and how the Word entered into the created world; another sequence (vv 6-8, 15) tells in a very concrete way how John the Baptist prepared for the coming of the Word into the world. The two strands in the drama come together when the Word's identity is revealed — Jesus Christ (vv 16-18). This song is an echo of the first song of creation in Genesis 1 — it too opens, 'In the beginning. . . .'

THE SONG OF THE WORD (John 1:1-18)

THE WORD SEQUENCE

The Word and creation
1. In the beginning was the Word:
the Word was with God
and the Word was God.
He was with God in the beginning.
2. Through him all things came into being.
3. Not one thing came into being except through him.
4. What has come into being in him was life,
life that was the light of men;
5. and light shines in the darkness
and darkness could not overpower it.

THE WITNESS SEQUENCE
6. *A man came, sent by God.*
His name was John.
7. *He came as a witness,*
to bear witness to the light,
so that everyone might believe through him.
8. *He was not the light,*
he was to bear witness to the light.

The Word in the world
9. The Word was the real light
that gives light to everyone;
he was coming into the world.
10. He was in the world
that had come into being through him,
and the world did not recognise him.
11. He came to his own
and his own people did not accept him.
12. But to those who did accept him
he gave power to become children of God,
to those who believed in his name
13. who were born not of human stock
or human desire
or human will
but from God himself.
14. The Word became flesh,
he lived among us,
and we saw his glory,
the glory that he has from the Father
as only Son of the Father,
full of grace and truth.

15. *John witnesses to him. He proclaims:*
'This is the one of whom I said:
He who comes after me
has passed ahead of me
because he existed before me.'

WHO IS THE WORD TO WHOM JOHN WITNESSES?
16. Indeed, from his fullness we have, all of us, received —
one gift replacing another,
17. for the Law was given through Moses,
grace and truth have come through Jesus Christ.
18. No one has ever seen God;
it is the only Son,
who is close to the Father's heart,
who has made him known.

Exercise 55:   *Let the group dramatise the* Song of the Word *(or describe how it could be presented on video). The following points may be useful in preparing the drama:*

(a) *The 'Word Sequence' expresses the vast, eternal, infinite range of God's will; the 'Witness Sequence' is more down-to-earth and tangible. How would you bring out the contrast between them?*

(b) *Note how the 'Word Sequence' takes up some major themes from Genesis 1 — light and life. How would you portray these in your drama?*

(c) *The 'Witness Sequence' can be related to John 1:19-34. How would you show the earthy, desert-hardened person of John?*

(d) *Note how the 'Word Sequence' falls into two parts, 'The Word and Creation', and 'The Word in the World'. They share certain themes which are developed from one to the other. How would your drama portray this?*

— *The Word with God — now revealed to be Son with Father: a new insight into God. (vv 1 and 14)*

— *Life and the Word — what kind of life? What does it mean to be born 'from God himself'? (vv 2-4 and 12-13).*

— *Light overcoming darkness — who is the light, and what kind of darkness? (vv 5 and 9-11)*

(e) *The final sequence (vv 16-18), in which the 'Word' and 'Witness' strands merge, reveals who the Word is: the eternal design is made flesh in a very physical man, Jesus Christ. The older story of Creation, which came in the 'Law' mediated through Moses, is fulfilled in an utterly new Creation Story centred on Jesus of Nazareth, 'full of grace and truth'. How do you think that could be expressed in your drama?*

The 'Song of the Word' gives us new insights on Creation: it is centred on the Word who is the Son of God. There is no creation except that made through the Word of God. In the dramatic presentation of John 1, the 'Word Sequence' shows the unrolling of the eternal plan of God ('the plans of his heart from age to age' *(Ps 33:11)*), while the 'Witness Sequence' intercuts with the human preparation in time by John the Baptist — in fact, the final stages of the witness of the prophets. The climax is reached when the Word becomes flesh — and John can point to him and proclaim, 'This is the One!' Now it is seen that when God said in the beginning, 'Let there be light!', he had in mind the model of the One who was the 'Light of the world' (see John 3:19; 8:12; 12:46). The life that multiplied at the dawn of creation was a sacrament of a life that would come 'not of human stock or human desire or human will but from God himself'. The universe is filled with a life beyond our measuring.

Like the Story of Israel, the Creation accounts in both *Genesis* and *John* reveal our identity: they are about meaning as much as making. For Genesis, we are made in the image and likeness of God; for John, we are made to be children of God. And they tell us of God: He is the One who, by his Word, has made all things. But there is for John an even more intimate revelation of God: 'It is the only Son, who is close to the Father's heart, who has made him known'. God is Father.

In the Genesis stories of creation we read that 'God created man in the image of himself' *(Gn 1:27)*. The book of *Wisdom* says that Wisdom is the 'untarnished mirror of God's active power, and image of his goodness' *(7:26)*. In the letter of St Paul to the Colossians there is another new Creation Song which names Christ as 'the image of the unseen God':

The Colossians' Song (Colossians 1:15-20)

15. He is the image of the unseen God,
the first-born of all creation,
16. for in him were created all things
in heaven and on earth:
everything visible and everything invisible,
thrones, ruling forces, sovereignties, powers —
all things were created through him and for him.

In the beginning, all was made in, through and for Christ.

17. He exists before all things
and in him all things hold together,
18. and he is the Head of the Body,
that is, the Church.

Today: Christ, who was before the beginning, is of the same body with us! That is where we take part in continuing creation.

He is the Beginning,
the first-born from the dead,
so that he should be supreme in every way;
19. because God wanted all fullness to be found in him
20. and through him to reconcile all things to him,
everything in heaven and everything on earth,
by making peace through his death on the cross.

The end of the world: to be reconciled to God and find full meaning through the death of Christ. To forgive is to create.

Exercise 56: *Read the Colossians' Song carefully. Note the balance between the first part (vv 15-16) and the final part (vv 18b-20):*

Christ is the image of God.	*Christ is all fullness (pleroma)*
He is 'the first-born of all creation'.	*He is 'the first-born from the dead'.*
All things in heaven and on earth were created through him, in him	*All things in heaven and on earth will be reconciled through him*
and for him.	*to God.*

Note the central part (vv 17-18a), and the contrast between the eternal ('He exists before all things') and the present time ('he is the Head of the Body . . . the Church').

How would you read the Colossians' Song aloud so as to bring out these points?

A creation without Christ is a figment of the imagination — it just doesn't exist. The World was made with Christ in mind, 'through him and for him.' Creation is still in process: it is not just a matter of beginnings — of things having been made 'in the beginning' — but of bringing all things to their completion, to their fullness as God intended them to be. And that fullness is to be found in Christ: he is 'the first-born of all creation'. The Colossians' Song contains an enormous hope for the world.

But it is a shadowed hope: the world we know is filled with the pain of growth and change, and it is caught in the distress of sin. God's creation has been marred by sin; there is a disharmony, an estrangement, a wrongness in the world, so that if creation is to be brought to its fullness in Christ it has first to be reconciled to God. Once again, to forgive is to create. As Paul put it to the Corinthians, 'God was in Christ reconciling the world to himself, not holding anyone's faults against him' (see 2 Corinthians 5:17-21). In the Colossians' Song, the turning point of this reconciliation is the death of Christ on the cross. His death and resurrection were an act of peacemaking between God and creation. In his body, for each of us and for the whole world, he overcomes all the forces of death and diminishment, all that enslaves the world, all the powers of uncreation — he became 'the first-born from the dead'.

The central verses of the Song (vv 17-18a) give *us* a point of contact with this work of reconciliation/creation. Note how the writer puts in parallel two quite different statements about Christ:

> He exists before all things. . .
>
> and he is the Head of the Body. . .

What began before anything existed is now being continued in his Body, the Church. In other words, we too have a part to play in bringing the world to its completion, its fullness in Christ, even as we ourselves are being brought to completion.

Exercise 57:   *Three areas for discussion and reflection:*

(1)   In the world today, what would you describe as creative, *and what as* destructive? *How do we judge what is good for the world or for people? Has the Creation of the world anything to do with peace and justice and love?*

(2)   The Colossians' Song sees Christ as both the Beginning and the End of Creation, 'and he is the Head of the Body, that is, the Church'. In view of all that we have seen, do you think the Church *has a role in the creation of the world? What qualities does this demand of the Church? Does this help you to understand what the Church is? What does it mean to* your *life?*

(3)   Romans 8:14-25. This could become the starting point for a prayerful reflection in the group. What is the Spirit saying to us through this text, and how does that affect our attitude to the world around us?

5 THE KING IN ISRAEL

In this chapter we will be looking at the part played in Israel's story by the King in Jerusalem and, especially, the significance of the family of David.

5.1   THE MAKING OF A KING

To understand the role of the King of Israel's story, we need to retrace our steps a little, back to the time of Joshua and the entry of the people of Israel into the land of Canaan (around 1,200 BC).

Exercise 58:   *The following selection of texts tell part of the story of leadership among the People of Israel from Joshua to David (about 1200-1000 BC). Please read the texts, and for each one write out the main points of the story in the space provided:*

Joshua 1:1-5

Joshua 10:40-43;
        11:21-23

Judges 3:1-7

Judges 4:1-24

Judges 7:1-25

Judges 15:1-20

---

1 Samuel 11:1-15

---

1 Samuel 17:1-58

Some things become clear about the situation of the People of Israel in the Promised Land. They were strangers, intruders; they had to fight and take by force what had been promised to them. In the land of Canaan they were surrounded by powerful enemies (see Joshua 13:1-6), while they themselves were weak and unorganised. In the early years of the conquest of Canaan, as it is described in *Joshua*, they were very much aware of their condition as a people of several tribes with a common history. That history went back hundreds of years to their ancestors Abraham, Isaac and Jacob. They had been freed from slavery in Egypt by 'the God of your fathers', and they had made a Covenant with the same God on Mount Sinai. And now they renewed that Covenant in a splendid ceremony at Shechem (see Joshua 24:1-28).

But as the years passed, and they became more integrated into the life and customs of Canaan, they tended to lose touch with one another, and even with their God (see Judges 2:11-15). They became an easier prey for their powerful enemies. Thus it happens that the book of *Judges* tells a tale of one crisis succeeding another, with a warrior of charismatic power raised up to lead some tribe or group of tribes to victory each time. Deborah, Gideon, Jephthah, Samson — one after another they played their parts, but there was no abiding union between the tribes.

Eventually, after about two centuries of hazardous existence in Canaan, there was a change of mood among the people. Perhaps their confidence was badly shaken when the Ark of the Covenant was captured by the Philistines (1 Samuel 4:1-22). Perhaps they longed for 'progress' — at that time the use of iron, whether in war or peace, was a monopoly of the Philistines (see 1 Samuel 13:19-22). Whatever the case, they asked the prophet Samuel for a king — 'Give us a king to rule over us, like the other nations' (1 Samuel 8:5). Saul was the first to be proclaimed king, but in reality he was more in the line of the charismatic 'judges' (see 1 Samuel 10:17 - 11:15). It is with David that a true monarchy is established, with a dynasty that would rule in Jerusalem for over 400 years.

Exercise 59:   *The following texts, from the Psalms, 2 Samuel and 1 Kings, describe the founding of the House of David and the Covenant God made with him and his successors. Please read the texts, and for each one write out the main points of the story in the space provided:*

Psalm 78:54-72

---

2 Samuel 5:1-12

---

2 Samuel 7:1-17

Already, in dealing with the City of Jerusalem, we have seen how David brought the Ark of the Covenant into the City, thereby making it the Spiritual Capital of the Israelites, the Holy City (see Chapter 3.1 p. 35). The texts in Exercise 59 speak more of David himself and his family. God made a promise that he would never desert David or his descendants: 'Your dynasty and your sovereignty will ever stand firm before me and your throne be forever secure' (*2 S 7:16*). Immediately, of course, this raised the problem of the succession: there were no precedents to determine which of David's sons should succeed him. David had many problems with his children, and in the end the succession question was solved by the intrigues of Bathsheba and the prophet Nathan. Where a dynasty is concerned, wives are important — and so are weddings! In Psalm 45 the poet sets out to praise the King and his bride — much as a 'poet laureate' might do today.

Psalm 45   A Royal Wedding Song

2. My heart overflows with noble words.
   To the king I must speak the song I have made;
   my tongue as nimble as the pen of a scribe.

Poet announces his intention. He dedicates his song to the King on his wedding.

3. You are the fairest of the children of men
   and graciousness is poured upon your lips:
   because God has blessed you for evermore.
4. O mighty one, gird your sword upon your thigh;
   in splendour and state, 5. ride on in triumph
   for the cause of truth and goodness and right.
   Take aim with your bow in your dread right hand.
6. Your arrows are sharp: peoples fall beneath you.
   The foes of the king fall down and lose heart.
7. Your throne, O God, shall endure for ever.
   A sceptre of justice is the sceptre of your kingdom.
8. Your love is for justice; your hatred for evil.
   Therefore God, your God, has anointed you
   with the oil of gladness above other kings:
9. your robes are fragrant with aloes and myrrh.

The King goes to meet his bride. *The poet praises not just his beauty or the splendour of his clothes, but the justice and integrity he stands for*

From the ivory palace you are greeted with music.
10. The daughters of kings are among your loved ones.
    On your right stands the queen in gold of Ophir.

The King returns with his bride.

11. Listen, O daughter, give ear to my words:
    forget your own people and your father's house
12. So will the king desire your beauty:
    He is your lord, pay homage to him.
13. And the people of Tyre shall come with gifts,
    the richest of the people shall seek your favour.

Praise for the beauty of the bride, and the role she is to play.

83

14. The daughter of the king is clothed with splendour,
    her robes embroidered with pearls set in gold.
15. She is led to the king with her maiden companions.
16. They are escorted amid gladness and joy;
    they pass within the palace of the king.

> *All enter the palace with great joy and splendour.*

17. Sons shall be yours in place of your fathers:
    you will make them princes over all the earth.
18. May this song make your name for ever remembered.
    May the peoples praise you from age to age.

> *A Blessing: this wedding will lead to many sons; the house and name of David are assured*

Psalm 45 was possibly a secular wedding song originally, perhaps not even an Israelite song (see the reference to 'the people of Tyre' in v 13). If so, it was adapted by the psalmist for the wedding of a king of the House of David. Besides praising the beauty of the royal couple, the song also stresses the concern of the king 'for the cause of truth and goodness and right' (v 5, see also vv 7-8. And see Chapter 5.3, p.90). The climax of the song is in the blessing that concludes it — the hope is that this marriage will ensure the continuity of the family of David, with sons to take over the throne in their turn.

Exercise 60:   *Enact Psalm 45. Can you say what you have learned from enacting this psalm? Why do people rejoice so much at royal weddings, even today?*

5.2   THE DEFENCE OF THE REALM

In a sense, the most obvious role of the king in Jerusalem was a military one — to unite and strengthen the people of Israel against their enemies. It is not surprising that there are some psalms that concern the king as leader of his people in time of war. The Israelites had not drifted so far from God as to forget entirely where their true strength lay; so they prayed for the king, the Lord's Anointed, both before and after battle.

Psalm 20

A prayer for the king before battle: strength of arms is helpful, but our deepest trust lies elsewhere:

> Some trust in chariots or horses,
> but we in the name of the Lord.
> They will collapse and fall,
> but we shall hold and stand firm.   *vv 8-9*

In this confidence they pray that God will give victory to the king, and grant him his 'heart's desire' (*v 5*).

Psalm 21

This psalm is like a response to the preceding one: the battle is over, the victory has indeed gone to the king:

> You have granted him his heart's desire;
> you have not refused the prayer of his lips.   *v 3*

Because the king has put his trust in God he has been victorious. The psalm is full of the heady, simple joy of winning, the relief at danger that has passed: God will continue to wipe out our (and his!) enemies; they will be swallowed up, they and their children. The earth will know their presence no more!

Psalm 60

Prayer for a time of war. The fortunes of war are going against the people of God. They are broken and weary and desperate.

People

3. O God, you have rejected us and broken us.
   You have been angry; come back to us.
4. You have made the earth quake, torn it open.
   Repair what is shattered for it sways.
5. You have inflicted hardships on your people
   and made us drink a wine that dazed us.
6. You have given those who fear you a signal
   to flee from the enemy's bow.
7. O come and deliver your friends,
   help with your right hand and reply.

They feel God has abandoned them, even though they are his people, those who fear him, his friends. That is what makes their present state so dreadful. They call for a word from him.

Prophet

8. From his holy place God has made this promise;
   'I will triumph and divide the land of Shechem,
   I will measure out the valley of Succoth.
9. Gilead is mine and Manasseh,
   Ephraim I take for my helmet,
   Judah for my commander's staff.
10. Moab I will use for my washbowl;
    on Edom I will plant my shoe.
    Over the Philistines I will shout in triumph'.

God replies in a prophecy; he has promised to be with them, and to use them against his enemies. He will triumph, and they will share his victory.

King

11. But who will lead me to conquer the fortress?
    Who will bring me face to face with Edom?
12. Will you utterly reject us, O God,
    and no longer march with our armies?
13. Give us help against the foe:
    for the help of man is vain.
14. With God we shall do bravely
    and he will trample down our foes.

In the anxiety of the war, with the tide of battle running against them, the king looks for an immediate fulfilment of the prophecy.

The background of Psalm 60 is probably the destruction of Jerusalem in 587 BC and the desperate times leading up to that. At that time, the people of Edom took the side of the Babylonians against Jerusalem (see comments on Psalm 137 in Chapter 3.6). To the anxious pleadings of the people (vv 3-7) God replies through the mouth of a prophet (vv 8-9). The original conquest of the land of Canaan will be repeated: Succoth and Shechem will be given back to the Israelites, along with the territory of the people of Gilead and the tribes of Manasseh and Ephraim. More than that, the neighbouring nations — and traditional enemies of the people of Israel — Edom, Moab and Philistia will be handed over to the Israelites too. Heartened by this prophecy, the king asks that God would mount an offensive straight away — especially against Edom! (vv 11-14)

I will triumph and divide
   the land of *Shechem*,
I will measure out
   the valley of *Succoth*.
Gilead is mine
   and *Manasseh*,
Ephraim I take
   for my helmet,
Judah for my
   commander's staff.

Moab I will use
   for my washbowl;
On *Edom* I will plant
   my shoe.
Over the *Philistines*
   I will shout in triumph.

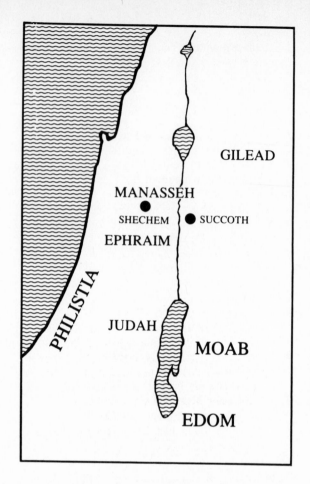

    The experience of wartime emergencies was a familiar one to the Israelites, and it gave rise to a number of psalms asking for divine help in battle. One of these, Psalm 108, is particularly interesting because it borrows the prophetic response and the final prayer of the king from Psalm 60:7-14 (the occasion may have been another time of hostilities with Edom). To these verses from Psalm 60 the writer attached a new set of opening lines, in which the king, as it seems, addresses a prayer of praise and thanksgiving to God. The result is a new psalm, again a prayer for God's help in time of battle, but without the desperate urgency of Psalm 60.

Psalm 108   A Prayer for Victory

Psalm 57

	King
8	2. My heart is ready, O God; I will sing, sing your praise.
9	Awake, my soul;
	3. awake, lyre and harp. I will awake the dawn.
10	4. I will thank you, Lord, among the peoples, among the nations I will praise you,
11	5. for your love reaches to the heavens and your truth to the skies.
12	6. O God, arise above the heavens; may your glory shine on earth.

The king speaks in praise of God; a prayer of thanksgiving. Only at the end does he ask for God's help — now!

Psalm 60:7	7. O come and deliver your friends; help with your right hand and reply.
	Prophet

8	8. From his holy place God has made
	    this promise:
	'I will triumph and divide the land of
	    Shechem;
	I will measure out the valley of
	    Succoth.

9	9. Gilead is mine and Manasseh. Ephraim I take for my helmet, Judah for my commander's staff.
10	10. Moab I will use for my washbowl, on Edom I will plant my shoe. Over the Philistines I will shout in triumph.'
	King
11	11. But who will lead me to conquer the fortress? Who will bring me face to face with Edom?
12	12. Will you utterly reject us, O God, and no longer march with our armies?
13	13. Give us help against the foe: for the help of man is vain.
14	14. With God we shall do bravely and he will trample down our foes.

God's reply

The king calls for help in the present crisis.

Psalm 108, then, is a composite psalm, not an original song at all. At some time, an unknown psalmist replaced the desperate opening section of Psalm 60 with a song of thanksgiving. Not only does this change the tone of the psalm, but it cuts out the voice of the people altogether. In the 'new' psalm 108, it is the king alone who prays and who is answered in prophecy. But the king's song of thanksgiving (Ps 108:2-6) is not original either — it comes from Psalm 57, where it has a different role to play, and has a different speaker!

Psalm 57 'I was helpless, so he saved me'

2. Have mercy on me, God, have mercy
   for in you my soul has taken refuge.
   In the shadow of your wings I take refuge
   till the storms of destruction pass by.
3. I call to God the Most High,
   to God who has always been my help.
4. May he send from heaven and save me
   and shame those who assail me.
   May God send his truth and his love.
5. My soul lies down among lions,
   who would devour the sons of men.
   Their teeth are spears and arrows,
   their tongue a sharpened sword.

The cry of someone surrounded by savage enemies. He relies on God who has 'always been my help'.

6. O God, arise above the heavens;
may your glory shine on earth!

Refrain, sung by the people as they listen to the story

	7. They laid a snare for my steps, my soul was bowed down. They dug a pit in my path but fell in it themselves.	*The singer's experience of how God answered his prayer*

Psalm 108		
2	8. My heart is ready, O God; I will sing, sing your praise. 9. Awake, my soul,	*The singer rejoices in his salvation — he wants to tell the whole world!*
3	awake, lyre and harp, I will awake the dawn.	
4	10. I will thank you Lord among the peoples, among the nations I will praise you	
5	11. for your love reaches to the heavens and your truth to the skies.	
6	12. **O God, arise above the heavens; may your glory shine on earth!**	*The people respond with the refrain.*

Exercise 61:   *The best way to understand these psalms and the relationships between them is by acting them out. Let the group enact Psalms 60, 57 and 108 (perhaps best in that order). Note how the meaning and significance of a passage can be changed when it is placed in a new context. Discuss this in the group, and ask yourselves: Do you think the meaning of a psalm can be affected when it is put in the context of our lives today? (For example: the psalms that speak of the king — what meaning do they have for us? Or the psalms that call for deliverance from enemies?)*

Psalms 20, 60 and 108 are all songs about the king in time of battle, calling on God to help him. There are also songs of thanksgiving after the king has led the people to victory. Psalm 21 is one of these, as is Psalm 118, which may be the text of a liturgical celebration in the Temple after a victory over one of Israel's great enemies. The centrepiece of the psalm is the king's own song of thanksgiving, and the whole psalm may have been performed in the following way:

Psalm 118   A victory celebration

1. Alleluia! Give thanks to the Lord for he is good, for his love has no end.	THEME — *see Psalms 106, 107, 136 etc.*
Choirmaster: 2. Let the sons of Israel say: 'His love has no end'. 3. Let the sons of Aaron say: 'His love has no end'. 4. Let those who fear the Lord say: 'His love has no end'.	LITURGICAL DIALOGUE — *see Psalms 115:9-11, 135:19-20*
King: 5. I called to the Lord in my distress; he answered and freed me. 6. The Lord is at my side; I do not fear. What can man do against me?	SONG OF THANKSGIVING: *Trust in God*

7. | The Lord is at my side as my helper:
   | I shall look down on my foes.
8. | It is better to take refuge in the Lord
   | than to trust in men:
9. | It is better to take refuge in the Lord
   | than to trust in princes.

10. | The nations all encompassed me;
    | in the Lord's name I crushed them.
11. | They compassed me, compassed me about;
    | in the Lord's name I crushed them.
12. | They compassed me about like bees;
    | they blazed like a fire among thorns.
    | In the Lord's name I crushed them.
13. | I was thrust, thrust down and falling
    | but the Lord was my helper.

Testimony — what God did for the king

14. | The Lord is my strength and my song;
    | he was my saviour.
15. | There are shouts of joy and victory
    | in the tents of the just.
    | The Lord's right hand has triumphed;
16. | his right hand raised me up.
    | The Lord's right hand has triumphed.
17. | I shall not die, I shall live
    | and recount his deeds.
18. | I was punished, I was punished by the Lord,
    | but not doomed to die.

Praise the Lord, for I live to tell the tale.

King:
19. Open to me the gates of holiness:
    I will enter and give thanks.

Gateman:
20. This is the Lord's own gate
    where the just may enter.

King:
21. I will thank you for you have given answer
    and you are my saviour.

DIALOGUE AT TEMPLE GATE — *see Psalms 15;24*

People:
22. The stone which the builder rejected
    has become the cornerstone.
23. This is the work of the Lord,
    a marvel in our eyes.
24. This day was made by the Lord;
    we rejoice and are glad.
25. O Lord, grant us salvation;
    O Lord, grant success.

SONG OF JOY *as the king enters the Temple*

Priests:
26. Blessed in the name of the Lord
    is he who comes.
    We bless you from the house of the Lord;
27. The Lord God is our light.

A BLESSING

| (Go forward in procession with branches even to the altar.) |] | INSTRUCTIONS *(for the people?)* |

King:
| 28. You are my God, I thank you.
My God, I praise you. |] | CONCLUDING PRAYER *(at the altar?)* |

| 29. Give thanks to the Lord for he is good;
for his love has no end. |] | THEME |

Exercise 62:   *Let the group enact Psalm 118, assigning people to the various parts. What is given here is, of course, only a conjectural reconstruction of the way the psalm was originally performed.*

Two discussion topics:
1. *Do you think God 'marches with our armies' today?*
2. *Psalm 118 would have been among those sung at the Last Supper by Jesus and his apostles. Do you think it could have had a special significance for Jesus at that time? What meaning does it have for you?*

5.3 THE ENEMY WITHIN

From its inception, the Kingdom ruled by David and his family was threatened by enemies from without — the neighbouring small nations of Edom, Moab, Philistia etc. and, at different times, the great empires of Egypt, Assyria, Babylon and Persia. It was the king's duty to preserve the integrity of his country against these aggressors. But there was another enemy, an enemy within, which proved to be an even greater threat to the existence of the people of Israel.

The Law of Israel was like a constitution for the country, and it guaranteed, if not equality, at least fair treatment for all the people.

> You will not be unjust in administering justice. You will neither be partial to the poor nor overawed by the great, but will administer justice to your fellow-citizens justly.   *Lv 19:15*

In the world of trade and commerce the same strict standards were to apply:

> You will not be unjust in administering justice as regards measures of length, weight or capacity. You will have just scales, just weights, a just *ephah* and a just *hin*. *Lv 19:35-36*
> (An *ephah* was a measure of dry capacity, about 45 litres; a *hin* measured 7.5 litres in liquids)

The very story of Israel itself should be enough to ensure that the weak and disadvantaged — the poor, widows, orphans, strangers, refugees — were treated not only justly but with kindness, 'for you yourselves were once aliens in Egypt' (*Lv 19:37*). And there were attempts to write into the statute books a system of provisions to safeguard family property and the freedom of individuals from enslavement (see Leviticus 25:1-55; Deuteronomy 15:1-18).

It was the duty of the king to ensure the safety and dignity of his subjects, and to stand against those who would wish to exploit the poor and defenceless. Poverty is not just a matter of lacking money or possessions. The poor are those who no longer have control of their own lives. As Psalm 10 puts it:

> The poor man is devoured by the pride of the wicked;
> he is caught in the schemes that others have made. *Ps 10:2*

To be caught and controlled by external forces is to be poor, whether it means being homeless or hungry, being made redundant because of economic depression, being forced to wait unnecessarily or to bribe public servants to get what one is already entitled to, having one's rights abused because of the power-struggles of others. . . . In so many ways one can be poor, and the very structures of a country's economy or its laws can serve to crush the powerless — those who are 'caught in the schemes that *others* have made'. In circumstances such as these, the people felt they should have in their king a protector. Such a protector would have prayed Psalm 101, proclaiming his own integrity and his determination to ensure justice for his people.

Psalm 101   The king is a just judge.

It seems there were regular court sessions held in the mornings in Jerusalem, at some of which at least the king may have presided. There were warnings from the prophets against corrupt practices:

> To the Royal House of Judah. Listen to the word of Yahweh, House of David!
> Yahweh says this:
> Each morning give fair judgement,
> rescue anyone who has been wronged
> from the hands of his oppressor. . .   *Jr 21:11-12 (See 22:1-3)*

So, in Psalm 101 the king proclaims his own uprightness, incorruptibility, justice; his refusal to mix with 'the crooked', the 'false-hearted', the 'man who practises deceit'. His law courts offer a fair opportunity to those who seek justice:

> Morning by morning I will silence
> all the wicked in the land,
> uprooting from the city
> all who do evil. (*v 8*)

Psalm 72

Of all the kings in Jerusalem none was more famous for his wise judgements than Solomon, to whom this psalm is dedicated. Solomon had asked one gift of the Lord: 'Give your servant a heart to understand how to govern your people, how to discern between good and evil, for how could one otherwise govern such a great people as yours?' (see 1 Kings 3:4-15). This psalm prays for the same gift in the king so that the people may enjoy justice, peace and prosperity in the land. Note how the psalm swings from the immediate concerns of the poor to the general condition of the realm.

1. O God, give your judgement to the king, to a king's son your justice,
2. so that he may judge your people in justice and your poor in right judgement.
3. May the mountains bring forth peace for the people and the hills, justice.
4. May he defend the poor of the people and save the children of the needy. and crush the oppressors.

The king as champion of justice and defender of the poor

Shalom

5. He shall endure like the sun and the moon from age to age.
6. He shall descend like rain on the meadow, like raindrops on the earth.
7. In his days justice shall flourish and peace till the moon fails.
8. He shall rule from sea to sea from the Great River to earth's bounds.
9. Before him his enemies shall fall, his foes lick the dust.

Peace, prosperity, expansion of the nation's power — all come to the just king. An idealised picture, based on the extent and wealth of Solomon's short-lived domain which stretched from the borders of Egypt to the River Euphrates (see 1 Kings 5:1-14; 10:1-29)

10. The kings of Tarshish and the sea coasts
    shall pay him tribute.
    The kings of Sheba and Seba
    shall bring him gifts.
11. Before him all kings shall fall prostrate,
    all nations shall serve him.

12. For he shall save the poor when they cry
    and the needy who are helpless.
13. He will have pity on the weak
    and save the lives of the poor.
14. From oppression he will rescue their lives,
    to him their blood is dear.
15. (Long may he live,
    may the gold of Sheba be given him.)
    They shall pray for him without ceasing
    and bless him all the day.

*The king and the poor:
he is to mediate God's
justice. It is God who first
of all hears the cry of the
poor!*

16. May corn be abundant in the land
    to the peaks of the mountains.
    May its fruit rustle like Lebanon;
    may men flourish in the cities
    like grass on the earth.
17. May his name be blessed for ever
    and endure like the sun.
    Every tribe shall be blessed in him,
    all nations bless his name.

*Peace (shalom) and
prosperity — the harmony
between humans and the
land has been restored
(see Genesis 3:17-19). And
the promise to Abraham
has been fulfilled (see
Genesis 12:1-3).*

* * *

18. Blessed be the Lord, God of Israel,
    who alone works wonders,
19. ever blessed his glorious name,
    Let his glory fill the earth.
    Amen! Amen!

*Not strictly speaking part of
Psalm 72, but a concluding
doxology to the group of
Psalms 42-72 (see Chapter
1.5)*

All this was the ideal; the reality was sadly otherwise. There was as much cruelty, oppression, intolerance and injustice among the people of Israel as in any other nation. It was a constant theme with the prophets:

> Listen to this, you who crush the needy
> and reduce the oppressed to nothing,
> you who say, 'When will the New Moon be over
> so that we can sell our corn,
> and Sabbath, so that we can market our wheat?
> Then we can make the bushel-measure smaller
> and the shekel-weight bigger
> by fraudulently tampering with the scales.
> We can buy up the weak for silver
> and the poor for a pair of sandals,
> and even get a price for the sweepings of the wheat'.
>
> *Am 8:4-6 (See 2:6-8; 5:10-15)*

And the kings, whether in Judah or in the breakaway Northern kingdom of Israel, were equally liable to betray their obligations to the weak and defenceless. David arranged the murder of Uriah the Hittite in order to take his wife Bathsheba (2 Samuel 11); Ahab and Jezebel arranged the death of Naboth in order to acquire his family property (1 Kings 21; and see Samuel's warning in 1 Samuel 8:10-18). The nobles and members of the royal families were allowed free rein in plundering the land:

> O my people, their oppressors pillage them
> and extortioners rule over them!
> O my people, your rulers mislead you
> and efface the path you ought to follow!
> Yahweh has risen to accuse,
> is standing to pass judgement on the people.
> Yahweh is about to try
> the elders and the princes of his people,
> 'You are the ones who have ravaged the vineyard,
> the spoils of the poor are in your houses.
> By what right do you crush my people
> and grind the faces of the poor?'
> says the Lord Yahweh Sabaoth.   *Is 3:12-15*

Exercise 63:   *Do these words from the Prophets and the Psalms apply to rulers today? Has the Church a duty to oppose injustice? Can you describe any unjust practices or situations in your country or in your community; can you suggest any action the Church could take on them? Do you see injustice as a problem in your own life?*

5.4 THE LORD'S ANOINTED

It was through the prophet Samuel that the first kings were named for the people of Israel. Saul and David were each anointed by the prophet, and each in turn was seized by the Spirit of God (see 1 Samuel 9:26 - 10:12; 16:13). Anointing with oil became the recognised ritual whereby a new king was established (see 1 Kings 1:39, Solomon; 2 Kings 9:6, Jehu; 11:12, Jehoash). From this the king was regarded as the Anointed One (in Hebrew, *Messiah*; in Greek, *Christ*). Strictly speaking, the king in Jerusalem — *any* king — was the Messiah.

Each king was seen to have a special relationship with God, and he inherited the promises first made to the great king, David. Thus, as the fortunes of the country waned, as the neighbouring powers of Egypt, Babylon or Assyria took control, the king — the Messiah — became a focus for the hopes of the people. And even after the terrible disaster of 587 BC and the destruction of the Temple and City of Jerusalem, the hope persisted. The psalms of the king were still sung — of his enthronement, his prowess in battle, his wedding, his wisdom and justice — but now they began to express *a hope for the future*. This hope looked to a time when the glories of David would be restored, when the occupying powers would be driven from the land, when peace and justice would be seen again in a land ruled by a member of the Royal House of David. In short, they began to long for the Messiah, the One who was still to come.

The final step in this development of meaning in the Psalms was taken when the Awaited One did finally come. The early Christian Church saw that Jesus was the fulfilment of the Scriptures, he was the answer to the hopes of Israel: 'Then he told them, "This is what I meant when I said while I was still with you, that everything written about me in the Law of Moses, in the Prophets and in the Psalms, was destined to be fulfilled" ' (*Lk 24:44*).

St Augustine called Jesus, 'the Singer of the Psalms'. He was a *Jew*, and so, of course, sang the Psalms many times in prayer. But even more than that, the Psalms were his songs because he was a *human being*. 'Becoming as human beings are' (*Ph 2:17*), and so sharing in the joys and sorrows and growth of a human being, Jesus experienced the 'life-situations' that lie behind the Psalms.

John 15:25
'They hated me without reason' — a frequent theme in psalms of sorrow and lament (Psalm 35:19; 69:4).

John 13:18
'He who shares my table takes advantage of me' — betrayal by a trusted friend (Psalm 41:9; 55:12-14).

John 2:17
'Zeal for your house will be the death of me' (*Ps 69:9*).
Anyone who forthrightly stands for God will attract the wrath of the wicked, as in the famous Temple incident (John 2:13-22). (In the Synoptic Gospels, this fatal confrontation comes towards the end of Jesus' life: Matthew 21:12-13; Mark 11:15-19; Luke 19:45-48.)

Exercise 64:   *For each of the following verses from the Psalms, find the relevant incident in the life of Jesus. (Psalm text given as it appears in the New Testament reading.)*

1. *By the mouths of children, babes in arms,*
   you have made sure of praise.   Ps 8:2

2. *I will speak to you in parables,*
   unfold what has been hidden
   since the foundation of the world.   Ps 78:2

3. *I said, you are gods.*   Ps 82:6

4. *He has given his angels orders about you.*
         and
   They will carry you in their arms
   in case you trip over a stone.   Ps 91:10-12

5. *The Lord declared to my Lord,*
   take your seat at my right hand,
   till I have made your enemies your footstool.   Ps 110:1

But if Jesus was a Jew, and a man, he was also the *Messiah*: the New Testament writers, reflecting the faith of the early Church, showed how they saw the fulfilment of the Scriptures in Jesus. He is the Christ, *Christos* (the Greek translation of the Hebrew word, *Messiah* or Anointed). Jesus was truly the King in Israel. We will look at some of the psalms of the king, and see how they were explored by the early Church in its search for the meaning of Jesus.

Psalm 118   (see Chapter 5.2, page 88)

As we have seen, this is a celebration for victory in battle: the king tells the tale to the people, and then they all enter the Temple together to give thanks to God. As with the other psalms of the king in Jerualem, Psalm 118 took on a messianic meaning in the minds of the Jewish people; it spoke of the Messiah who was to come. In this sense it was taken up by the early Christians who saw it as referring to Jesus. The psalm came to describe another triumphal entry — that of Jesus into Jerusalem.

> Great crowds of people spread their cloaks on the road, while others were cutting branches from the trees and spreading them in his path. The crowds who went in front of him and those who followed were all shouting:
> Hosanna to the son of David!
> Blessed is he who is coming in the name of the Lord!
> Hosanna in the highest heavens!   *Mt 21:8-9*

94

Note that the cry 'Hosanna!' literally means, 'Save, please!' and it may derive from v 25 — 'grant us salvation'. In the psalm, 'he who comes' refers to the king who is being blessed 'in the name of the Lord'. The New Testament quoting of the verse changes it to read, 'Blessed is he who is coming in the name of the Lord!' This underlines its new significance, that Jesus is the hoped-for One of the House of David (see Matthew 11:3 — 'Are you the one who is to come, or are we to expect someone else?').

In Psalm 118, as I have described it in Chapter 5.2, the people sing a song of joy and wonder as the king enters the Temple:

> 22. The stone which the builder rejected
>   has become the corner stone.
> 23. This is the work of the Lord,
>   a marvel in our eyes.

They are, of course, referring to the king's recent victory over his enemies, but their song became for the early Christians a song of joy at the triumph of Jesus. Peter speaks to the rulers and elders of the people after the healing of a lame man:

> You must know, all of you, and the whole people of Israel, that it is by the name of Jesus Christ the Nazarene, whom you crucified, and God raised from the dead, by this name and by no other that this man stands before you cured. This is the stone which you, the builders, rejected but which has become the cornerstone. Only in him is there salvation; for of all the names in the world given to men, this is the only one by which we can be saved.
>
> *Ac 4:10-12*

The balance in Peter's argument is clear — Jesus was crucified ('rejected' by the builders) and then raised from the dead ('became the cornerstone'). This is truly the work of the Lord!

The same stress on rejection is found in *Matthew 21:42* where this text from Psalm 118 forms a commentary on the parable of the wicked tenants (21:33-43) in which the tenants saw the son of the owner coming and 'they said to each other, "This is the heir. Come on, let us kill him and take over his inheritance." So they seized him and threw him out of the vineyard and killed him'. Jesus too was taken outside the city and killed. The parable (which ends with a threat of punishment for the murderous tenants) is brought into a resurrection context by the addition of Psalm 118:22-23 — the 'son' and 'heir' has indeed been rejected, but by God's power, he will 'become the cornerstone'.

These verses of Psalm 118 appear elsewhere in the New Testament too, e.g. Luke 20:17-18; 1 Peter 2:4-8, and see Ephesians 2:20. Clearly, they were one of the earliest and most fertile sources of inspiration in the reflections of the early Church on the death and resurrection of Christ.

Psalm 110 is part of a liturgical action at the enthronement of the king in Jerusalem. Quoted more often in the New Testament than any other psalm, even before the time of Jesus it was interpreted as referring to the Messiah. Martin Luther said of it, 'This is the high and chief Psalm of our dear Lord Jesus Christ, in which his Person, and his Resurrection, Ascension, and his whole kingdom. . . are clearly and powerfully set forth'.

Psalm 110   At the right hand of God

Prophet:

> 1. The Lord's revelation to my Master:
>   'Sit on my right:
>   your foes I will put beneath your feet'.

Prophecies about the king at his enthronement

2. The Lord will wield from Zion
   your sceptre of power:
   rule in the midst of all your foes.

3. A prince from the day of your birth
   on the holy mountains;
   from the womb before the dawn I begot you.

> 4. The Lord has sworn an oath he will not change.
>   'You are a priest for ever,
>   a priest like Melchizedek of old.'

People:

5. The Master standing at your right hand
   will shatter kings in the day of his wrath.

6. He, the Judge of the nations,
   will heap high the bodies;
   heads shall be shattered far and wide.

Words of encouragement from the people — God will be with the king in time of battle.

7. He shall drink from the stream by the wayside
   and therefore he shall lift up his head.

A liturgical directive?

Psalm 110 is part of an enthronement or coronation ceremony (or the anniversary of such) and it contains two prophecies (vv 1,4) spoken by a Temple prophet, with a commentary (vv 2-3) particularly suited to strengthen the king in time of danger from enemies. The people add their own words of encouragement (vv 5-6) — or so I suggest in the above reconstruction. The final verse (7) is very obscure; there may be something missing which would make the meaning clearer. Set in the context of a battle (verse 6) in which God takes a part, it may refer to the king pausing to quench his thirst before continuing with the matter in hand. It has also been suggested that, in the setting of an enthronement ceremony, this may be a liturgical directive referring to some kind of 'sacramental' drinking by the king as a sign of God's continuing support.

The meaning of this psalm, and in particular the meaning of v 1, had changed over the centuries of its use. Originally it concerned a king (or kings) in Jerusalem, which king we do not know. So v 1, spoken by a prophet, concerned a word of God to the king. However, in later years, when it was supposed that the psalm had been written by David, it took a new meaning. In this new meaning David is referring to a word of God addressed to the Messiah.

Psalm 110:1 'The Lord's revelation to my Master (my Lord)'

Original meaning: Prophet proclaimed God's word to the King ('my Master')

Later meaning: David proclaims God's word to the Messiah ('my Master')

In other words, in the later understanding of the psalm it was seen to refer to the Messiah, not just any king in Jerusalem. And it was in that sense that it was used by Jesus and the New Testament writers. See, for example, the verbal tussle between Jesus and some of the Jewish leaders when Jesus posed the question, 'What is your opinion about the Christ? Whose son is he?' They told him, 'David's'. He said to them, 'Then how is it that David, moved by the Spirit, calls him Lord, when he says: The Lord declared to my Lord. . .' (see Matthew 22:41-46).

Psalm 110:4 contains an oracle referring to Melchizedek, who is described in Genesis 14:18 — 'Melchizedek king of Salem brought bread and wine; he was a priest of God Most High.' The Genesis passage (14:17-19) describes a meeting between this 'King of Salem' and the patriarch Abraham. 'Salem' was, of course, taken to be Jerusalem (see Psalm 76:2), and the Davidic kings were seen in the light of this mysterious person who ruled in Jerusalem at the time of the Patriarchs, and who was both king and priest. So, in the enthronement ceremony for the king in Jerusalem there is this solemn proclamation of his priestly role as well (Psalm 110:4). The two roles of king and priest are found in the lives of several of the kings of David's house — see 2 Samuel 6:12-19 (David), 8:18 (David's sons); 1 Kings 8:14, 55-56, 62-63 (Solomon). All of this was transferred to the expected Messiah: Melchizedek became a symbol of the Messiah, who would also be both priest and king. It was this background of ideas that lay behind the letter to the Hebrews (see 4:14 - 5:10; 7:1-28). '. . . this one (Christ), because he remains for ever, has a perpetual priesthood. It follows, then, that his power to save those who come to God through him is absolute, since he lives for ever to intercede for them' *(7:24-25)*.

The most significant impact of Psalm 110 on the New Testament lies in the reference seen in v 1 to the ascension of Christ who 'has taken his seat at the right hand of the divine Majesty on high'. (see Hebrews 1:3).

Exercise 65:   *The following texts from the New Testament all contain references to Psalm 110:1. Please read them, and note relevant words or phrases in the space provided:*

Matthew 26:64

Acts 2:33-36

Romans 8:34

1 Corinthians 15:25-26

Ephesians 1:20

Colossians 3:1

Hebrews 1:13

Hebrews 10:12-13

To realise the significance of Psalm 110 we need to remember the way the Apostles and the early Church approached the problem of understanding Christ. His life, miracles, preaching and personality had all made an enormous impact on those who met him. But despite the apparent efforts of Jesus himself, nothing could have prepared the disciples for his death, still less for the events that followed it. They simply had no way of understanding what had happened, no language to express these events which were completely without precedent. So they did what the poets and prophets had done before them: they turned to the events and writings and songs of the past to find the words they needed for the experiences of the present.

The *death of Jesus* was seen in the light of the significant deaths and sufferings of the past. The Psalms and the prophets contributed to the language of the crucifixion.

I have not turned my face away
from insult and spitting.   *Is 50:6*   Matthew 26:67

Like a lamb led to the slaughter-house,
like a sheep dumb before its shearers   Acts 8:32-35
he never opened his mouth.   *Is 53:7*   Matthew 27:14

Exercise 66:   *The following texts from Isaiah and the psalms are referred to in the account of Jesus' death and burial in* Matthew 27. *Please fill in the relevant verse numbers in the space provided.*

For food they gave me poison; in my thirst they gave me vinegar to drink	*Ps 69:22*	
They divide my clothing among them. They cast lots for my robe.	*Ps 22:19*	
All who see me deride me. They curl their lips, they toss their heads.	*Ps 22:8-9*	
My God, my God, why have you forsaken me?	*Ps 22:1*	
He was given a grave with the wicked, and his tomb is with the rich.	*Is 53:9*	

However, it was when they came to grips with the *resurrection and ascension of Jesus* that the early Christians most needed the help of the Psalms. If the suffering and death of Jesus could be seen as a fulfilment of the experiences described in the Psalms, then what happened to him *after* his death should also be in some way signalled in the Psalms. We have already seen that Psalm 118 was taken to hold a deeper meaning concerning Christ, pointing specifically to his being raised from the dead (see pp. 94-95). Similarly, Psalm 16 maintains an astonishing hope that the bond of love and life between God and the psalmist cannot be broken even by death:

8. I keep the Lord ever in my sight:
   since he is at my right hand, I shall stand firm.
9. And so my heart rejoices, my soul is glad;
   even my body shall rest in safety.
10. For you will not leave my soul among the dead,
    nor let your beloved know decay.
11. You will show me the path of life,
    fullness of joy in your presence,
    at your right hand happiness for ever.

Peter, speaking at Pentecost, comments that David (who he assumed had written Psalm 16) was speaking of Christ: 'Since he was a prophet, and knew that God had sworn him an oath to make one of his descendants succeed him on the throne, he spoke with foreknowledge about the resurrection of the Christ: he is the one who was not abandoned to Hades, and whose body did not see corruption.' (*Ac 2:30-32*)

The real significance of what happened to Jesus after his death is not that he *came back* to life (as, for instance, Lazarus had done in John 11), but that he *went on* to a new level of life beyond our understanding. In the post-resurrection appearances in the gospels, he is the same Jesus, yet so strangely different, even at times unrecognisable. But how could the early Christians express something they could not themselves understand? This is where Psalm 110 made its most important contribution. The prophecy that the Messiah (as it was understood) would be seated at the right hand of God became a language for saying that Jesus had taken the place of honour and equality with the Father: 'For this reason the whole House of Israel can be certain that the Lord and Christ whom God has made is this Jesus whom you crucified' (*Ac 2:36*). Filled with this new meaning, Psalm 110:1 became an integral part of the Gospel, and of our way of speaking about Jesus to this day: our creeds have it — 'He ascended into heaven and is seated *at the right hand* of the Father.' The impact of this psalm on the early Church can be seen in the great number of times it is referred to in the New Testament writings (The examples in Exercise 65 are only a small sample). In the gospel tradition handed on by Paul he says that 'on the third day (Christ) was raised to life, *in accordance with the scriptures*' (*1 Co 15:4*). Most certainly Psalm 110 was one of the scriptures in question. Another was Psalm 2.

Psalm 2   A part of a liturgy on the occasion (or the anniversary) of the king's enthronement

1. Why this tumult among nations,
   among peoples this useless murmuring?
2. They arise, the kings of the earth,
   princes plot against the Lord and his Anointed.
3. 'Come, let us break their fetters,
   come, let us cast off their yoke'.

> The scene on earth*: other rulers reject the (new) king and in doing so they reject God too!*

4. He who sits in the heavens laughs;
   the Lord is laughing them to scorn.
5. Then he will speak in his anger,
   his rage will strike them with terror.
6. "It is I who have set up my king
   on Zion, my holy mountain."

> The scene in heaven: *God rejects the other rulers, and supports the king in Jerusalem.*

7. I will announce the decree of the Lord:
   The Lord said to me: 'You are my son.
   It is I who have begotten you this day.
8. Ask and I shall bequeath you the nations,
   put the ends of the earth in your possession.
9. With a rod of iron you will break them,
   shatter them like a potter's jar.'

> *A prophet (or the king himself?) speaks the word of God: the king is God's son, i.e. he has a special relationship with God.*

10. Now, O kings, understand,
    take warning, rulers of the earth;
11. serve the Lord with awe
    and trembling, pay him your homage
12. lest he be angry and you perish;
    for suddenly his anger will blaze.

> *Warning to the other rulers of the earth: all are to 'serve the Lord'. This is the real message of the psalm — that the God of Jerusalem is the LORD of all the earth*

Blessed are they who put their trust in God.

> *Response: sums up the whole psalm*

Psalm 2 is another psalm taken from an enthronement or anniversary celebration. As with Psalm 110, the enthronement of a king is an occasion for words of encouragement, but also for proclaiming the significance of the king in Israel's story. The coronation of a new king in Jerusalem provokes a hostile reaction from neighbouring rulers, but as the psalm sees it, their opposition is to both 'the Lord and his Anointed' (*vv 1-3*). In turn, God rejects them and stands by the king whom he has himself established 'on Zion, my holy mountain' (*vv 4-6*). Into this situation of tension between heaven and earth (which would reflect an actual political tension between Israel and the neighbours) the prophetic word is spoken: God proclaims his special relationship with the Davidic king — 'You are my son. It is I who have begotten you this day' (*v 7*).

In view of the strict monotheism of Judaism, the term 'son' here cannot have any stronger meaning than some kind of adoption: the king is taken by God into a family relationship. As Psalm 89 expresses it,

27. He will say to me: 'You are my father,
    my God, the rock who saves me.'
28. And I will make him my first-born,
    the highest of the kings of the earth.

29. I will keep my love for him always;
    with him my covenant will last.

As with the other psalms of the king in Jerusalem, Psalm 2 took on a messianic meaning in the hopes of Israel, but it was not until the psalm was applied to Jesus that a deeper sense was seen in it.

Exercise 67:   *The following texts from the New Testament all contain references to Psalm 2. Please read them and note relevant words and phrases in the space provided:*

Acts 4:23-28

Acts 13:32-35

Hebrews 1:1-5

Luke 3:21-22

Such psalms as 2, 16, 110 and others gave a firm ground to the early followers of Christ as they tried to formulate who he was and what he had done. In doing this, they went far beyond the original life-situations of those psalms to a new setting in the *Gospel*: 'This is the gospel concerning his Son who, in terms of human nature was born a descendant of David and who, in terms of the Spirit and of holiness was designated Son of God in power by resurrection from the dead: Jesus Christ our Lord' (*Rm 1:1-4*).

Of course, God does not have a right hand for anyone to sit by, as the psalmist and the apostles well knew. It is a manner of speaking, a way of pointing to the place of highest honour and equality given to Jesus by God. It is another way of saying that 'Jesus is Lord'. Nor does God have a Son, in the strict biological sense. Jesus is the (biological) son of Mary; to say he is Son of God is a way of expressing the intimacy between him and God, their common divine nature, and especially their relationship. To say that Jesus is Son is to say that God is a parent, whom Jesus calls 'Father'.

Exercise 68:   *Of the following terms which* five *do you think best describe God?*

Almighty	Gentle	Terrible	Unchanging
Intimate	Creator	Loving	Judge
Mother	King	Suffering	Faithful
Lord	Listening	Warrior	Father
Mysterious	Wise	Humble	Compassionate

Share in small groups why you chose these five terms. Can you say how much your idea of God is shaped by the story of Jesus, and how much by other influences?

100

6 GOD, AND OTHER QUESTIONS

In this chapter we will see some more of what the Psalms teach us about God. In the last analysis, all the stories of the Bible are stories of God, and the Psalms are sung in his praise.

6.1 BROKEN PROMISES

The faith of Israel is rooted in the faithfulness of God. As the story of Israel reveals, he is a listening God, one who hears the cry of distress and is strong to answer it. There is a pattern to his pity that is celebrated in the Psalms:

> How gracious is the Lord, and just;
> our God has compassion.
> The Lord protects the simple hearts;
> I was helpless so he saved me. *Ps 116:5-6*

When the Israelites were helpless he saved them and made them his people: he bound his story to theirs by a covenant and a king. And he gave them commandments and laws and customs, as Moses reminded the people: 'Keep them and put them into practice: such is Yahweh's command to you. Stray neither to right nor to left. Follow the whole way that Yahweh has marked for you, and you will survive to prosper and live long in the country which you are going to possess' (*Dt 5:32-33*).

To live according to the commandments of God is to be assured of his blessing. The first psalm establishes this as an introductory theme for the whole Psalter.

Psalm 1 The waters of a good life

1. Happy indeed is the man
   who follows not the counsel of the wicked;
   nor lingers in the way of sinners
   nor sits in the company of scorners,
2. but whose delight is the law of the Lord
   and who ponders his law day and night.

Happiness flows from choosing rightly: see Deuteronomy 30:15-20, when Moses gave the people a choice — 'life or death, blessing or curse'.

3. He is like a tree that is planted
   beside the flowing waters,
   that yields its fruit in due season
   and whose leaves shall never fade;
   and all that he does shall prosper.

   Possibly based on Jeremiah 17:8 — to trust in God is to drink deeply of the water of life.

4. Not so are the wicked, not so!
   For they like winnowed chaff
   shall be driven away by the wind.
5. When the wicked are judged they shall not stand,
   nor find room among those who are just;

   In contrast, to abandon God is to abandon 'the fountain of living water' (Jr 2:13).

6. for the Lord guards the way of the just
   but the way of the wicked leads to doom.

   The two ways: 'Choose life, then, so that you may live... (Dt 30:19)

This psalm sums up for the individual the ideal relationship between a faithful people and a faithful God. But there was another experience within the story of Israel, one in which virtue is no guarantee of prosperity, and God is not faithful or reliable. There were times, for Israel, when God broke his own promises. Psalm 44 records one such experience: the people sing of their faithfulness to God (vv 2-9), which contrasts with God's rejection of them (vv 10-17). They complain bitterly at the unfairness of this (vv 18-23) and finally call to God strenuously, that at least for the sake of his love he should help them (vv 24-27).

Psalm 44 Is God our enemy now?

2. We heard with our own ears, O God,
   our fathers have told us the story
   of the things you did in their days,
   you yourself, in days long ago.

   The Story — the faithfulness of God and the trust of the people. All as it should be.

3. To plant them you uprooted the nations:
   to let them spread you laid peoples low.
4. No sword of their own won the land;
   no arm of their own brought them victory.
   It was your right hand, your arm
   and the light of your face: for you loved them.
5. It is you, my king, my God,
   who granted victories to Jacob.
6. Through you we beat down our foes;
   in your name we trampled our aggressors.
7. For it was not on my bow that I trusted
   nor yet was I saved by my sword:

   The voice of the king?

8. it was you who saved us from our foes,
   it was you who put our foes to shame.
9. All day long our boast was in God
   and we praised your name without ceasing.

10. Yet now you have rejected us, disgraced us:
    you no longer go forth with our armies.
11. You make us retreat from the foe
    and our enemies plunder us at will.
12. You make us like sheep for the slaughter
    and scatter us among the nations.
13. You sell your own people for nothing
    and make no profit by the sale.

    The pattern is changed: God is an enemy now! He has rejected us, so that all can laugh at us. God cuts his losses, and gets rid of his people at any price.

14. You make us the taunt of our neighbours,
    the laughing-stock of all who are near.
15. Among the nations, you make us a byword,
    among the peoples a thing of derision.
16. All day long my disgrace is before me:
    my face is covered with shame

Again, the king speaks?

17. at the voice of the taunter, the scoffer,
    at the sight of the foe and avenger.

18. This befell us though we had not forgotten you;
    though we had not been false to your covenant,
19. though we had not withdrawn our hearts;
    though our feet had not strayed from your path.
20. Yet you have crushed us in a place of sorrows
    and covered us with the shadow of death.
21. Had we forgotten the name of our God
    or stretched out hands to another god
22. would not God have found this out,
    he who knows the secrets of the heart?
23. It is for you we face death all day long
    and are counted as sheep for the slaughter.

And why should God have abandoned us? We have not abandoned him! This is the most disturbing aspect of the whole affair — God is not being faithful to his own promises. He cannot be relied upon.

24. Awake, O Lord, why do you sleep?
    Arise, do not reject us for ever!
25. Why do you hide your face
    and forget our oppression and misery?
26. For we are brought down low to the dust;
    our body lies prostrate on the earth.
27. Stand up and come to our help!
    Redeem us because of your love!

Enough of this! God has slept long enough; let him awake and redeem us for his love's sake if for no other reason. And in the end, what better reason?

A similar situation is described in Psalm 89, which has much the same outline as Psalm 44. In the case of Psalm 89, however, the story focuses on King David and the extraordinary promises made to him and his family.

Psalm 89   A Deserted King

vv 1-38   God the Creator and Saviour made a covenant with David:

> I will establish his dynasty for ever,
> make his throne endure as the heavens. . .
> I will never violate my covenant
> nor go back on the word I have spoken.   *vv 30,35*

vv 39-46   A litany of broken promises:

> You have broken your covenant with your servant. . .
> You have made all his enemies rejoice.   *vv 40,43*

vv 47-52   How long, O Lord? — a question only God can answer.

Psalms 74 (see chapter 3.6) and 77 carry the same protest, the same desperate perplexity at the unreliability of God:

> This is what causes my grief:
> that the way of the Most High has changed   *Ps 77:11*

What is so terrifying about the experiences reflected in these psalms is that they undermine the very foundations of Israel's faith. For God to reject his people when they were unfaithful is understandable; it happened often enough in Israel's history. But even then God was consistent, he kept his word, his punishments were justified. But for Yahweh wilfully to desert his people, to forget his mother-love for them, is for him to be reduced to the level of the idols — unfriendly, capricious, deadly. The story has lost its meaning, and God his identity. We don't know who God is anymore, nor do we know who we are ourselves. That is why these psalms keep reaching back to the events that identify God, his great saving and creating deeds (see Pss 44:2-6; 74:13-17; 77:12-21; 89:2-13). It is a problem of faith, of clinging to a God who has changed out of all recognition.

Perhaps the most awful of these psalms of abandonment is Psalm 88.

Psalm 88 *'There was darkness over the whole land'*

1. Lord, my God, I call for help by day;
   I cry at night before you.
2. Let my prayer come into your presence.
   O turn your ear to my cry.
3. For my soul is filled with evils;
   my life is on the brink of the grave.
4. I am reckoned as one in the tomb:
   I have reached the end of my strength,
5. like one alone among the dead;
   like the slain lying in their graves;
   like those you remember no more,
   cut off, as they are, from your hand.

The cry of distress — the psalmist is as good as dead already.

6. You have laid me in the depths of the tomb,
   in places that are dark, in the depths.
7. Your anger weighs down upon me:
   I am drowned beneath your waves.
8. You have taken away my friends
   and made me hateful in their sight.
   Imprisoned, I cannot escape;
9. my eyes are sunken with grief.

Accusation: it is God who is the enemy. The singer is friendless, lonely, shut in, ravaged by grief, and it is all God's doing!

   I call to you, Lord, all the day long;
   to you I stretch out my hands.
10. Will you work your wonders for the dead?
    Will the shades stand and praise you?
11. Will your love be told in the grave
    or your faithfulness among the dead?
12. Will your wonders be known in the dark
    or your justice in the land of oblivion?
13. As for me, Lord, I call to you for help:
    in the morning my prayer comes before you.

He is already among the dead, where no word of love and faithfulness can reach, where there is no memory. Yet still he calls to God — something the dead cannot do.

14. Lord, why do you reject me?
    Why do you hide your face?
15. Wretched, close to death from my youth,
    I have borne your trials; I am numb.
16. Your fury has swept down upon me;
    your terrors have utterly destroyed me.
17. They surround me all the day like a flood,
    they assail me all together.
18. Friend and neighbour you have taken away:
    my one companion is darkness.

Bleak finish to a dreadful prayer. God is hidden, and there remain only chaos, water and the darkness of the time before creation (see Chapter 4.1 and 4.2). But God is still 'You'!

In Psalm 88 there is no appeal to God's saving and creating deeds in the past, no reference to the Story, only the most fleeting mention of the 'wonders' worked by his 'love' and 'faithfulness'. The anguish of the psalmist is too pressing to allow him much thought for the past. He meets no tangible hope, but neither does he turn away from the God-become-enemy: the most important word in the psalm, and the one most often repeated, is 'you'. In all his dark agony, the psalmist is on the threshold of accepting God without any story — just for himself alone.

Exercise 69:   *Either A or B could be the basis for small group discussion.*

A   *Some questions to think about:*
Have you ever had any experience like that recounted in Psalm 88?
What do you do when God refuses to answer your prayers?
Is God a friend to you? Why do you love God?

B   *Read the following extracts from the story of Cecilia Pak, a twenty-eight-year-old Korean leper:*

I got leprosy at the age of seven. A leper has to be got rid of fast. Even those who love you tell you to kill yourself. It is the best way out for everybody. . . . Everyone I met kept telling me to do away with myself. My parents came out and took me to a deep river and embraced me and hugged me and cried goodbye: my father in his numb way, my mother with streams of tears and crying. After they'd gone, I cried until I cried myself dry. . . . And though I knew that way for me was the only way out for my parents to live — and I only seven years old — I couldn't go into the river even to stop the terrible pain of hunger in my belly. . . .

There was no hope, but I lived here and there hiding in the fields. Sadness and tears were my only friends then. I roamed with death and pain always behind me. . . . After a few years on the roads I met Ko Joseph, an old leper, and his non-leper wife, Martha, who had settled as squatters on mountain land and built a mud house for themselves and for other lepers. All are welcome to all he has in his small hut here, and to the little that he may have in it. All are also welcome to all that he hopes yet to do for his fellow lepers — which coming from the wideness of Joseph's heart is in no way small. . . .

The poor among us lepers are damned. If a rich man gets leprosy he can buy his way into an established leper colony. But why must we destitute lepers live every day in our sad hunger with death walking always by our side? We are here heaped on top of one another in the pain of trying to keep alive. It feels like life is one hard lump of sadness and pain that can't be taken out.

Suicide always sits beside each of us. Since I became a leper I have lived twenty-one years with suicide beside me as my only promising friend. At least in trying to write this there rises down deep in me the faint hope that God or someone somewhere like him will put a sure bite in our mouth every bad hungry sunrise that we drag ourselves out into another vague formless day in which none of us are alive or dead. Yet I am lucky to be alive in a way. It must be God. It has to be better than suicide. . . .

When I came here first I tried going into town to Mass on Sundays; but I don't go there anymore because I couldn't bear it when the Catholics nearest me all edged themselves away like I was a prisoner or something. They made me feel like a leper. Here with the other lepers, at least I don't feel like a leper!

What would you say to Cecilia Pak? Could you live by what you would say to her? (Extract from the Far East, *1975)*

This encounter with the dark side of God is found throughout the story of Israel. Sometimes it is seen as a just punishment for sin (see Psalms 78, 79 and 106), sometimes as a time of testing by God (see Deuteronomy 8:2-6). But there were times when the encounter was more mysterious, more terrifying.

Abraham:
In fulfilment of his promise God gave Abraham and Sarah an heir (see Genesis 12:1-3; 15:1-6; 21:1-7), then he demanded the death of this 'son, your only son, your beloved Isaac' *Gn 22:1-10.* Who is this God who would ask such a thing? It is not just that Isaac is to be killed, but that God has broken his own promise: what of the 'great nation' if the only heir is to die? Have the ways of the Most High changed?

Jeremiah
preached against the people because they had abandoned God, 'the fountain of living water, and dug water-tanks for themselves, cracked water-tanks that hold no water' (see Jeremiah 2:13; 17:7-8 and Psalm 1). Yet the prophet's own experience of God was a very cruel one (see Jeremiah 15:10-11; 20:7-18). In his desperation he turns God's own water-talk back on him: 'Why is my suffering continual, my wound incurable, refusing to be healed? Truly, for me you are a deceptive stream with uncertain waters!' (*Jr 15:18*)

Job's
sufferings were at God's hands, the God who 'for no reason, wounds and wounds again, not even letting me regain my breath, with so much bitterness he fills me!' (*Jb 9:17-18*). Job rejects all the usual explanations for his plight, but in the end gets no satisfactory answer to all his questioning.

Lamentations 3
is the song of someone who has suffered greatly at the hands of God: 'For me he is a lurking bear, a lion in hiding. Heading me off, he has torn me apart, leaving me shattered. He has bent his bow and used me as a target for his arrows.' And still the singer clings to God: 'Yahweh is all I have,' I say to myself, 'and so I shall put my hope in him' (*v 24*).

Psalm 88 describes a return to chaos in the life of the psalmist. God is hidden, silent, uncaring, absent. There remain only the flood waters of the deep, and darkness (vv 14-18). The singer has been uncreated. This is an experience of utter loss; the only life-line remaining is the cry of the singer to the God who is still 'You'. The question is not just whether the singer can survive this dreadful loss, but can *God* survive it?

God is similarly tested in the lives of others in the story of Israel: Abraham, Jeremiah, Job etc. There are many today for whom the evil of the world has become so tangible and terrible as to blot out the God of love. There are those whose image of God has proved inadequate to the complexity of life; their prayers have gone unanswered, and they feel betrayed and abandoned. And some have been led along the path of faith to a meeting with the utter mystery of God: their senses and understanding break down in a Dark Night of the Soul filled with dread. Somewhere along this line, Jesus too lost touch with the God of his ancestors, and cried out in an agony of loneliness.

Psalm 22 contains the lonely desperation of someone who feels abandoned by his God. According to two of the Gospels, the opening words of this psalm were spoken from the cross by Jesus (see Matthew 27:45-46; Mark 15:33-34). By Hebrew convention, to cite the opening words in this way can be taken as referring to the psalm in its entirety. Other verses of Psalm 22 are echoed in the accounts of Jesus' passion and death (see vv 7,8,18).

Psalm 22 *'A man of sorrows, familiar with suffering'*

1. My God, my God, why have you forsaken me?
   You are far from my plea and the cry of my distress.
2. O my God, I call by day and you give no reply;
   I call by night and I find no peace.

3. Yet you, O God, are holy,
   enthroned on the praises of Israel.
4. In you our fathers put their trust;
   they trusted and you set them free.
5. When they cried to you, they escaped.
   In you they trusted and never in vain.

6. But I am a worm and no man,
   the butt of men, laughing-stock of the people.
7. All who see me deride me.
   They curl their lips, they toss their heads.
8. "He trusted in the Lord, let him save him;
   let him release him if this is his friend."

9. Yes, it was you who took me from the womb,
   entrusted me to my mother's breast.
10. To you I was committed from my birth,
    from my mother's womb you have been my God.
11. Do not leave me alone in my distress;
    come close, there is none else to help.

12. Many bulls have surrounded me,
    fierce bulls of Bashan close me in.
13. Against me they open wide their jaws,
    like lions, rending and roaring.

14. Like water I am poured out,
    disjointed are all my bones.
    My heart has become like wax,
    it is melted within my breast.
15. Parched as burnt clay is my throat,
    my tongue cleaves to my jaws.

16. Many dogs have surrounded me,
    a band of the wicked beset me.
    They tear holes in my hands and my feet.
16c. and lay me in the dust of death.
17. I can count every one of my bones.
    These people stare at me and gloat;
18. they divide my clothing among them.
    They cast lots for my robe.

19. O Lord, do not leave me alone,
    my strength, make haste to help me!

20. Rescue my soul from the sword,
    my life from the grip of these dogs.
21. Save my life from the jaws of these lions,
    my poor soul from the horns of these oxen.

DISTRESS & TRUST
The God-who-hears-the-cry is deaf! (see Isaiah 49:14; 54:7-8)

The Story of Israel is the basis for his trust in God now.

The psalmist's sufferings have stripped him of his humanity; he is an object of derision (see Isaiah 52:13 - 53:12; Psalm 102).

The singer's own story: if God is not there, that story is already over.

ENEMIES
— *Bulls*

— *Lions*

His body, his life — fading away (see Psalms 38:7-8; 102:1-11)

— *Dogs*
— *Armed men*

Let the Lord rescue him from the enemies around him:
— *Armed men*
— *Dogs*
— *Lions*
— *Bulls*

22. I will tell of your name to my brethren
and praise you where they are assembled.

23. 'You who fear the Lord give him praise;
all sons of Jacob, give him glory.
Revere him, Israel's sons.

24. For he has never despised
nor scorned the poverty of the poor.
From him he has not hidden his face,
but he heard the poor man when he cried.'

25. You are my praise in the great assembly.
My vows I will pay before those who fear him.

26. The poor shall eat and shall have their fill.
They shall praise the Lord, those who seek him.
May their hearts live for ever and ever!

27. All the earth shall remember and return to the Lord,
all families of the nations worship before him

28. for the kingdom is the Lord's; he is ruler of the nations.

29. They shall worship him, all the mighty of the earth;
before him shall bow all who go down to the dust.

30. And my soul shall live for him, my children serve him.
They shall tell of the Lord to generations yet to come,

31. declare his faithfulness to peoples yet unborn:
'These things the Lord has done.'

A SONG OF PRAISE
among friends

Testimony: *what God has done for me*

The song of praise rings through the Temple; all who hear it gain hope, and themselves begin to sing. . .

The whole world sings, even the gentiles; and can it be that even those in the dust of death are praising God?

It all becomes part of the Story to be told for generations. . .

Psalm 22 falls into two parts so different from each other that they may originally have been two distinct psalms: vv 1-21 and vv 22-31.

vv 1-21 is an agonised, bitter protest against unendurable loneliness. Through all the aggression of the singer's enemies and the ravages on his person, his most basic sorrow has to do with God. Why should God be so unGodlike as to abandon him? Repeatedly he cries, 'Do not leave me alone!' (*vv 11,19*). He turns to the Story of Israel (vv 3-5) and to his own story (vv 9-10) and finds traces of God there — but of God *now* there is no sign, no reply. Has God, then, changed? Has he left the singer alone against his enemies? They crowd around him, crushing him like bulls and savaging him like lions; they snap at him like dogs and tear him with swords (vv 12-13, 16). He begins to collapse under the assault, but continues to appeal to God for help (vv 20-21 repeat the images of his enemies: armed men, dogs, lions, bulls).

vv 22-31 is quite different. In contrast to the short phrases and sharp movements of the first part of Psalm 22, the rhythm is slower, more spacious. The enemies crowding around have been replaced by the Great Assembly in the Temple. The core of the singer's testimony, which is to be broadcast to the whole world, is that God is, after all, faithful — to himself and to the 'poor man when he cried'.

These psalms of broken promise touch on the mystery of God. How can God abide with so much that is wrong and evil in the world? And how can we believe in a God who stays silent in the face of so much suffering? The Psalms give no answer to that, except perhaps that the flood waters and darkness (Psalm 88:17-18) may be the prelude to a new creation. Or it may be that the only hope lies in the One who himself entered the heart of the darkness but kept his trust in God. 'Jesus cried out in a loud voice saying, "Father, into your hands I commit my spirit" ' — and the psalm continues, 'It is you who will redeem me, Lord' (see Luke 23:46; Psalm 31:6).

108

Exercise 70: Read Psalm 22. How would you dramatise it so as to bring out the suffering and loneliness of the singer, and his joyful reunion with his friends in the Great Assembly?

Discussion: If, as St Paul says, 'he emptied himself, taking the form of a slave, becoming as human beings are' (Ph 2:7), could Jesus too have shared the dark encounter with God that so many people experience? Do you think that Jesus in his agony felt that the ways of the Most High had changed? Does Psalm 22 help us to understand the meaning of Jesus' passion and death? Did Jesus need to be redeemed?

6.2 GOD IS LOVE

Once, greatly daring, Moses asked to see the face of God. It was too much to ask, 'for no human being can see me and survive'. Yet God did reveal something of himself to Moses, and he

> passed before him and called out, 'Yahweh, Yahweh, God of tenderness and compassion, slow to anger, rich in faithful love and constancy, maintaining his faithful love to thousands, forgiving fault, crime and sin, yet letting nothing go unchecked, and punishing the parent's fault in the children and in the grandchildren to the third and fourth generation.' (see Exodus 33:18 - 34:9)

This experience of God entered into the language of prophecy and poetry, and is found in one form or another throughout the writings of Israel. It became part of the Israelites' basic understanding of God, and as such was handed on from generation to generation. And it lies at the heart of several psalms that tell of the *hesed* of God, his faithful love.

Psalm 86 The love of God through sorrow, joy and perseverance

1. Turn your ear, O Lord, and give answer
   for I am poor and needy.
2. Preserve my life, for I am faithful:
   save the servant who trusts in you.
3. You are my God, have mercy on me, Lord,
   for I cry to you all the day long.
4. Give joy to your servant, O Lord,
   for to you I lift up my soul.
5. O Lord, you are good and forgiving,
   full of love to all who call.
6. Give heed, O Lord, to my prayer
   and attend to the sound of my voice.
7. In the day of distress I will call
   and surely you will reply.

The pattern of God's pity: the singer calls to God 'in the day of distress'. There are, as yet, no details of his need, just a statement of trust in the God who listens and who will surely reply.

8. Among the gods there is none like you, O Lord;
   nor work to compare with yours.
9. All the nations shall come to adore you
   and glorify your name, O Lord:
10. for you are great and do marvellous deeds,
    you who alone are God.
11. Show me, Lord, your way
    so that I may walk in your truth.
12. I will praise you, Lord my God, with all my heart
    and glorify your name for ever;
13. for your love to me has been great:
    you have saved me from the depths of the grave.

A sudden song of praise at the greatness of God. And small wonder: this man almost died! But 'you have saved me from the depths of the grave'. God has opened a space for him, he has a future, and so he asks a further blessing: to know the way

14. The proud have risen against me;
    ruthless men seek my life:
    to you they pay no heed.
15. But you, God of mercy and compassion,
    slow to anger, O Lord,
    abounding in love and truth,
16. turn and take pity on me.
    O give your strength to your servant
    and save your handmaid's son.
17. Show me a sign of your favour
    that my foes may see to their shame
    that you console me
    and give me your help.

The future is hope; the present is still dangerous. At last he names the enemy: men who care nothing for God. He relies on childhood lessons, the traditions of a 'God of mercy and compassion. . .' All he needs now is a sign which both he and his enemies might see. And the psalm ends there — a sign may or may not be given.

Psalm 86 is a heart-cry from the midst of trouble; the viewpoint is not of one looking back on an episode in the past, but of one still in a condition of need. The psalm moves through three stages: a cry to the God-who-Listens (vv 1-7); a song of praise to the God-who-gives-life (vv 8-13); and then back to the cry of distress (vv 14-17). The psalm does not have a happy ending: as it closes, the singer is still in great danger, desperately looking for a sign of God's favour. He has been left naked to his enemies; in his weakness he falls back on the traditions handed on by his parents, the rhythms of childhood lessons:

> God of mercy and compassion,
> slow to anger, O Lord,
> abounding in love and truth. (*v 15*)

These simple and comforting lines, echoes of Exodus 34:5-6, sustain his hope as he waits in the midst of his enemies for God to help him.

The Exodus experience of Yahweh, God of mercy and compassion, is further developed in Psalm 103. In this psalm we see how an individual's own personal experience of God's love and forgiveness can enlarge his heart and his vision. For the psalmist, the whole creation and the story of Israel speak of the mercy (*hesed*) of God, just as he himself does in the depths of his own soul.

Psalm 103 *Love and Creation*

vv 1-5 This song of praise bursts out of the soul of the psalmist; his inmost being has been touched by the mercy of God — forgiveness, healing, life and vitality. He has not only been saved from death, but his youthful vigour has been restored to him. He is a 'born again' worshipper, and he is swept by a new enthusiasm for God's love in the world.

vv 6-18 The story of Israel: the psalmist takes up the Exodus 34 description of God (v 8) with a special stress on his mercy and forgiveness: where Exodus 34 spoke of God's punishments on children and grandchildren, Psalm 103 assures us, 'his wrath will come to an end; he will not be angry for ever' (*v 9*). God's justice puts him on the side of the oppressed (v 6); he forgives even those who deserve punishment (vv 10-12). He is like a compassionate father to us (v 13). All this, even though (or perhaps, *because*) we are no more than wind-blown dust (vv 14-16). It is God's love for us that gives us stability and life: we are *everlastingly* held by his love and justice (vv 17-18).

110

vv 19-22   This awareness of God's nearness to such passing creatures as we are lifts the singer's mind to all creation. All thank God and sing his praises — the heavens, angels, stars, all the works of God, every place and time. The very fact of their existence is a praise of God: creation is a gift of God, a grace. The singer is in harmony with all creation; they sing the same song, they are equally graced by the love of God.

Exercise 71:   *The experience of a 'God of tenderness and compassion' revealed in Exodus 34:6-7 is taken up in various ways in other psalms and in the prophets. Read the following examples, and note the particular emphasis in each case:*

       Psalm 111:4   *(We remember the Lord, and his loving compassion.)*

       Psalm 145:8   *(The love of God in a world full of wonders)*

       Jeremiah 32:18   *(God's faithfulness as a basis for hope: why, do you think, has Jeremiah been told to buy a field? Read the whole passage, 32:1-44.)*

       Micah 7:18-20   *(God's tenderness a basis for hope)*

       Joel 2:12-14   *(A call to repentance)*

       Do you experience the 'God of tenderness and compassion' in your life? Perhaps you would like to share with a small group your own awareness of God's love for you.

The lovingness of God has led him into an involvement with us which endures for ever. This is no cold, casual relationship, but one which has the makings of great joy and much pain. To love is to make oneself vulnerable. Even the event of forgiveness and reconciliation has its own suffering, not to speak of the pain of rejection and loss. In a sense, by loving us God has put himself at *our* mercy. This too is a part of God's loving us, as the prophets saw with their inspired insight into the movements of God's heart. Some of the greatest love songs have to do with God's longing for his people.

The Song of the Vineyard   *(Isaiah 5:1-7, 27:2-5 RSV)*

The 'Song of the Vineyard' (Isaiah 5:1-5) is a drama. Just as Nathan the prophet led King David to judge himself (see 2 Samuel 12:1-12) so those who are listening to the Song are led to pass judgement on their own failure. The Song begins as a simple agricultural problem posed to the listeners, the 'inhabitants of Jerusalem and the men of Judah'; Isaiah (possibly with a companion in the part of the beloved, the owner of the vineyard) presents the case of a non-productive vineyard. What can be done about it? Probably they paused after v 4 in the singing of the song to allow for words of advice or suggestions from the audience. It is only when the singing continues with the 'owner's' words in vv 5 and 6, and Isaiah's revelation in v 7, that the real intent of the prophecy becomes clear: the vineyard is the house of Israel, the 'owner' is 'the LORD of hosts'! By that time, the responses of the listeners already stand in judgement upon them; they are condemned out of their own mouths.

The Song of the Vineyard expresses the desire of God for his people, and his bitter disappointment with them. Their wickedness and injustice have provoked an outcry against Jerusalem; they, whom the Lord had led to freedom, have themselves become oppressors. The background to this song is the social and religious disorders of the eighth century before Christ (see Isaiah 1:10-23; 3:12-15), a time when the Land and the City were also under threat from the Assyrian Empire.

5:1 1. Let me sing for my beloved
a love song concerning his vineyard:

My beloved had a vineyard
on a very fertile hill.
2. He digged it and cleared it of stones,
and planted it with choice vines;
he built a watchtower in the midst of it,
and hewed out a wine vat in it;
and he looked for it to yield grapes,
but it yielded wild grapes.

3. And now, O inhabitants of Jerusalem
and men of Judah,
judge, I pray you, between me
and my vineyard.
4. What more was there to do for my vineyard,
that I have not done in it?
When I looked for it to yield grapes,
why did it yield wild grapes?

*   *   *

5. And now I will tell you
what I will do to my vineyard.

I will remove its hedge,
and it shall be devoured;
I will break down its wall,
and it shall be trampled down.
6. I will make it a waste;
it shall not be pruned or hoed,
and briers and thorns shall grow up;
I will also command the clouds
that they rain no rain upon it.

7. For the vineyard of the LORD of hosts
is the house of Israel,
and the men of Judah
are his pleasant planting;
and he looked for justice,
but behold, bloodshed;
for righteousness,
but behold, a cry!

27:2 2. In that day:

A pleasant vineyard, sing of it!
3. I, the LORD, am its keeper;
every moment I water it.
Lest any one harm it,
I guard it night and day;
4. I have no wrath.
Would that I had thorns and briers to battle!
I would set out against them,
I would burn them up together.
5. Or let them lay hold of my protection,
let them make peace with me,
let them make peace with me.

Introduction

The Love Song, Part 1 —
*the prophet tells of the
failed vineyard.*

*The owner of the vineyard
speaks (the 'beloved' of
verse 1) — he calls on
the people of Judah to judge
the vineyard.*

*(Responses from
the listeners)*
*The owner reveals what he
intends to do to his
vineyard.*

The Love Song, Part 2 —
*the prophet reveals what the
vineyard really is: it is the
very people who have been
asked to judge the case!*

The Love Song, Part 3 —
*The owner takes up the
Love Song himself: he cares
for his vineyard; he longs
for his people to return to
him — 'let them make peace
with me'.*

At a later stage in Israel's history, long after Jerusalem had been destroyed and rebuilt, and the people had returned from captivity in Babylon, another (anonymous) prophet took up the theme of the Vineyard Song to draw it out in a more hopeful direction. (Isaiah 27:2-5. Isaiah 24-27, the so-called 'Apocalypse of Isaiah', though now contained within the book of *Isaiah*, were in fact composed by another prophet who lived probably around 450 BC — three centuries after Isaiah himself.) In this re-interpretation of the Vineyard Song, God wishes to restore his vineyard, he has no wrath against it any more, he still longs for his people. So, the Song of the Vineyard, in a new time and setting, retains its original message: God is passionately concerned about his people.

Exercise 72:   *How could the Song of the Vineyard be performed? Let some of the group enact the Song, with the following cast of characters: 'Isaiah', the 'owner', the 'inhabitants of Jerusalem' (who would make suitable suggestions after v 4).*

What have you learned from this drama?

Can you imagine what are the feelings of the 'owner for his vineyard?

What are God's feelings for you, *do you think?*

The passion of God for his people is a rich theme in the writings of the prophets:

> But look, I am going to seduce her
> and lead her into the desert
> and speak to her heart.
> There I shall give her back her vineyards,
> and make the Vale of Achor a gateway of hope.
> There she will respond as when she was young,
> as on the day when she came up from Egypt.   *Ho 2:16-17*

> Come home, Virgin of Israel,
> come home to these towns of yours.
> How long will you hesitate,
> rebellious daughter?
> For Yahweh is creating something new on earth:
> the Woman sets out to find her Husband again.   *Jr 31:21-22*

> Zion was saying, 'Yahweh has abandoned me,
> the Lord has forgotten me.'
> Can a woman forget her baby at the breast,
> feel no pity for the child she has borne?
> Even if these were to forget,
> I shall not forget you.
> Look, I have engraved you on the palms of my hands,
> your ramparts are ever before me.   *Is 49:14-16*

The language of human loving is used to describe God's love for us. The strongest bonds we know — between husband and wife, mother and child, friend and friend — can only hint at the depth of God's desire for us. The language of the prophets can seem very daring to us, even extravagant. Yet we miss its meaning entirely if we take it from its biblical context. Especially when they use the image of husband and wife the prophets are speaking of something more than a romantic attachment between God and us. The basis for this language lies in Genesis 2:23-24:

> And the man said:
>
> 'This one at last is bone of my bones
>   and flesh of my flesh!
> She is to be called Woman,
>   because she was taken from Man.'

> This is why a man leaves his father and mother and becomes
> attached to his wife, and they become one flesh.

What can we say of a God who so loves us that he desires to become 'one flesh' with us?

If it is hard for us to realise the intensity of God's love for us, it may be even harder to remember *who* it is that loves us. This 'tremendous lover' is terrifying and dangerous, powerful beyond all our imagining. With a word he creates the universe (Genesis 1); his very voice makes — and breaks!

Psalm 29 *Glory to God in the Highest!*

1. O give the Lord you sons of God,
   give the Lord glory and power;
2. give the Lord the glory of his name.
   Adore the Lord in his holy court.

A call to the angels to praise God in the heavenly courts (a praise to be echoed in the Temple — see v 10)

3. The Lord's voice resounding on the waters,
   the Lord on the immensity of waters;
4. the voice of the Lord, full of power,
   the voice of the Lord, full of splendour.
5. The Lord's voice shattering the cedars,
   the Lord shatters the cedars of Lebanon;
6. he makes Lebanon leap like a calf
   and Sirion like a young wild-ox.
7. The Lord's voice flashes flames of fire.
8. The Lord's voice shaking the wilderness,
   the Lord shakes the wilderness of Kadesh;
9. the Lord's voice rending the oak tree
   and stripping the forest bare.
   The God of glory thunders.

A violent storm rages over the Land, from Mount Lebanon and Hermon (Sirion) in the North to the desert at Kadesh-Barnea in the South. 'The voice of God', qol Yahweh, thunders seven times through these verses.

10. In his temple they all cry: 'Glory!'
    The Lord sat enthroned over the flood;
    the Lord sits as king for ever.

The thunder of God is matched by shouts in the Temple. God sits in serene majesty.

11. The Lord will give strength to his people,
    the Lord will bless his people with peace.

The storm-maker is also the peace-maker.

It has been suggested that Psalm 29 was based on a Phoenician hymn to a weather-god. If this is so, it has been completely taken over as a Hebrew prayer of praise and wonder: the *name* of the Exodus God, *Yahweh* (translated as 'Lord') is heard eighteen times in this short song! And it is this God, imaged in a terrifying storm, who loves us with the utmost tenderness and compassion.

What is it, then, to be loved by this great God? In this course we have seen how God is passionate about us; he is moved to pity, anger, tenderness, forgiveness and creativity because of his faithful love, his *hesed. We are*, because of his love.

> . . . God is love.
> This is the revelation of God's love for us,
> that God sent his only Son into the world
> that we might have life through him.
> Love consists in this:
> it is not we who loved God,
> but God loved us and sent his son
> to expiate our sins. *1 Jn 4:8-10*

What is it like to be loved by God? What is it like to be loved by *anybody*? The language of human loving enabled the prophets to tell of God as lover; the same language can be used to describe us as beloved. But here, each of us must speak for herself or himself, and share the joy, the grace, the serenity, the vision, the awakening, the enabling of being loved. Let me just point to two songs from the Scriptures that seem to me to have been born out of the experience of being beloved of God.

Psalm 144   *A strong man sings of the God who loves him*

This is a man's song, probably a king's.

vv 1-2
God is good, and we see his love for us in the good things of life: strength, health, protection in time of trouble, life itself. And for the King, victory and successful rule. 'He is my love', my *hesed*! God is love, and he is for me. So, the singer begins with a blessing, a joyful proclaiming of all that God is and has done for him.

vv 3-8
But love is a gift, and one of the effects of being loved is a sense of wonder — 'Why *me*?' Who am I that you should care for me? Real love cannot be earned; which makes it so often difficult to understand or even accept. The singer moves to a sense of his own nothingness; he is a puff of wind, a shadow (vv 3-4). And now, a deeper delight begins to fill his heart, for it is the *Creator* who loves him, the God of Genesis and Exodus. The psalmist turns to water-talk: God once again divides the 'mighty waters', and the singer is saved from his enemies (vv 5-8).

vv 9-11
A new song for an old love — the psalmist is in a long line of people whom God has loved, chief among them 'David your servant'. None of us owns God's love, nor is it diminished by being shared with others. We belong to a beloved *people*.

vv 12-15
Though it may have been a separate composition from vv 1-11, this closing part of the psalm in fact carries on the insights of the earlier verses. One of the effects of being loved is a desire that this love should be shared; the beloved sees the world with different eyes. So there is a prayer here for the whole people, for health and growth, for harmony and peace. May our sons and daughters, and all the people, and all creatures, and the whole land share in these blessings!

The second such love song is a woman's song, the *Magnificat* of Mary (Luke 1:46-55). It follows a pattern very similar to Psalm 144, and reflects the delight and wonder and vision of someone deeply aware of God's love for her.

Luke 1:46-55   *The Song of Mary*

My soul glorifies the Lord, my spirit rejoices in God, my Saviour.	*Blessing God, delighting in him, the beloved cannot contain her joy.*
He looks on his servant in her lowliness; henceforth all ages will call me blessed. The Almighty works marvels for me. Holy his name!	*'Why* me*?' She is filled with wonder at God's loving her. At the same time, the serene awareness of how blessed, how wonderful she is — they will be talking about this for generations!*

His mercy is from age to age,	*This same* hesed *(mercy/love) of God*
on those who fear him.	*has existed 'from age to age' —*
He puts forth his arm in strength	*he reaches out to those who can accept*
and scatters the proud-hearted.	*his love: the poor, the hungry,*
He casts the mighty from their thrones	*those who fear him, the* anawim. *Those*
and raises the lowly.	*who cannot accept his love are scattered.*
He fills the starving with good things,	*This is a new vision for the world.*
sends the rich away empty.	

He protects Israel, his servant,	*The Story — which is a love story —*
remembering his mercy,	*is of a people to which Mary belongs.*
the mercy promised to our fathers,	*The fulfilment of the promise 'to our*
to Abraham and his sons for ever.	*fathers' is found in Mary's Son.*

In this love-song we meet again the pattern of God's pity which we saw in Psalm 107 (see Chapter 2.4, pp. 26-27):

40. He pours contempt upon princes
    makes them wander in trackless waters.
39. They diminish, are reduced to nothing
    by oppression, evil and sorrow.
41. But he raises the needy from distress;
    makes families as numerous as a flock.
42. The upright see it and rejoice
    but all who do wrong are silenced.
43. Whoever is wise, let him heed these things
    and consider the love of the Lord.

God's love is a power to transform the world, a vision of new things.

God's love for Mary cannot be separated from his love for her Son. Jesus, above all others, is the Beloved: 'And when Jesus had been baptised he at once came up from the water, and suddenly the heavens opened and he saw the Spirit of God descending like a dove and coming down on him. And suddenly there was a voice from heaven, "This is my Son, the Beloved; my favour rests on him." ' (*Mt 1:16-17*; see 17:5, the Transfiguration) All the affection of the Father is focused on his Word-made-flesh, and we who are in Christ share in that love of God.

Thus he chose us in Christ before the world was made
to be holy and faultless before him in love,
marking us out for himself beforehand, to be adopted sons,
through Jesus Christ.
Such was his purpose and good pleasure,
to the praise of the glory of his grace,
his free gift to us in the Beloved. . . . *Ep 1:4-6*

To be loved by God is to be created and saved. And all this — love, creation, salvation — takes place through his only Son. God's desire for us is fulfilled through Jesus Christ: God has, in fact, become 'one flesh' with us in the Beloved!

Exercise 73:   *In the end, all the psalms and canticles of the Scriptures sing of the love of God. Now that we are almost at the end of this course in the Psalms, perhaps you would like to write a psalm of your own.*

Let each member of the group compose a psalm. These prayer-songs could be shared at a special meeting of the group, and even form the basis for praying together.

6.3 A MATTER OF LIFE AND DEATH

Death puts a question-mark against everything. No matter how wonderful the story, it comes to an end; every person, every project, every hope can be destroyed by death. Death is an inescapable fact of life.

Exercise 74:   *Discussion questions:*

What happens at death?

Have you had any experience of death — in your family, of a friend, violent or peaceful?

Can you recall the Christian teaching about death?

Do you know of any other teachings about death, for example in other religions such as Buddhism or Hinduism, or in the traditional religions of Africa or North America. . .?

For the Hebrews too death had to be faced. It was the common lot of all people, 'the way of all the earth' (see 1 Kings 2:2). In one line of thought, death was the great leveller: no matter how mighty the rich man became, he would one day lose all and be reduced to nothing:

> I have seen the wicked triumphant,
> towering like a cedar of Lebanon.
> I passed by again; he was gone.
> I searched; he was nowhere to be found. *Ps 37:35-36*

Death waits for everyone, and in a sense there is no tragedy in that. A man could die full of years, with dignity and decency, and 'be gathered to his ancestors' (see Deuteronomy 34:5-8, Moses; 1 Kings 2:10, David; Job 42:17 — 'Then, old and full of days, Job died'). To be cut off in one's prime was another matter: see the Canticle of Hezekiah:

> I thought: In the noon of my life
> I am to depart.
> At the gates of Sheol I shall be held
> for the rest of my days.
> I thought: I shall never see Yahweh again
> in the land of the living,
> I shall never see again a single one
> of those who live on earth.
> My home has been pulled up, and thrown away
> like a shepherd's tent;
> like a weaver, I have rolled up my life,
> he has cut me from the loom. *Is 38:10-12*

Dying can be a sudden thing, or the body can slowly and painfully diminish, disintegrate and wither away. One such dreadful passing is described in Psalm 102. In fact, there seem to be two distinct psalms here: vv 1-11 and 23-28, the cry of a dying man; and vv 12-22, a prayer for Jerusalem.

Psalm 102

1. O Lord, listen to my prayer
   and let my cry for help reach you.
2. Do not hide your face from me
   in the day of my distress.
   Turn your ear towards me
   and answer me quickly when I call.
3. For my days are vanishing like smoke,
   my bones burn away like a fire.

*The singer is dying,
and calls out to God:
'Do not turn away
from me!'*

117

4. My heart is withered like the grass.
   I forget to eat my bread.
5. I cry with all my strength
   and my skin clings to my bones.
6. I have become like a pelican in the wilderness,
   like an owl in desolate places.
7. I lie awake and I moan
   like some lonely bird on a roof.
8. All day long my foes revile me;
   those who hate me use my name as a curse.
9. The bread I eat is ashes;
   my drink is mingled with tears.
10. In your anger, Lord, and your fury
    you have lifted me up and thrown me down.
11. My days are like a passing shadow
    and I wither away like the grass.

12. But you, O Lord, will endure for ever
    and your name from age to age.

God hears, and has pity on Jerusalem.

13. You will arise and have mercy on Zion:
    for this is the time to have mercy,
    (yes, the time appointed has come)
14. for your servants love her very stones,
    are moved with pity even for her dust.
15. The nations shall fear the name of the Lord
    and all the earth's kings your glory,
16. when the Lord shall build up Zion again
    and appear in all his glory.
17. Then he will turn to the prayers of the helpless;
    he will not despise their prayers.
18. Let this be written for ages to come
    that a people yet unborn may praise the Lord;
19. for the Lord leaned down from his sanctuary on high.
    He looked down from heaven to the earth
20. that he might hear the groans of the prisoners
    and free those condemned to die;
21. that the name of the Lord may be proclaimed in Zion
    and his praise in the heart of Jerusalem,
22. when peoples and kingdoms are gathered together
    to pay homage to the Lord.

23. He has broken my strength in mid-course;
    he has shortened the days of my life.

Surely this same God will have pity on a dying man, this God who lives for ever.

24. I say to God: 'Do not take me away
    before my days are complete,
    you, whose days last from age to age.
25. Long ago you founded the earth
    and the heavens are the work of your hands.
26. They will perish but you will remain.
    They will all wear out like a garment.
    You will change them like clothes that are changed.
27. But you neither change, nor have an end.
28. The sons of your servants shall dwell untroubled
    and their race shall endure before you.'

The singer of this psalm is a young man who finds himself unexpectedly on the verge of death. His body is weakened by pain and fever, he is isolated and lonely, he is only a shadow of his former self (vv 1-11). He cries out against the unfairness of his condition; God, who lives for ever, will not allow him even his meagre life span:

> Do not take me away
> before my days are complete,
> you, whose days last from age to age. *v 24*

The psalm ends with confident praise of the everlasting God whose servants will live untroubled lives, 'and their race shall endure before you' (*vv 23-28*).

The extraordinary aspect of Psalm 102 is the sudden change in vv 12-22. (Even the poetical rhythm changes, and these verses may possibly have come from another source altogether.) It is as if a great love in the psalmist's heart triumphed over his weakness, for he begins to sing of Jerusalem! The disintegration of his body finds a parallel in the destruction of Jerusalem; for her too the forces of death threaten her very existence. And that is too much for the psalmist to bear. He prays for the City, and at the same time draws hope for himself from God's commitment to its protection:

> For the Lord leaned down from his sanctuary on high.
> He looked down from heaven to the earth
> that he might hear the groans of the prisoners
> and free those condemned to die. *vv 19-20*

Sheol and separation

What most horrified the Hebrews about death was its separation: for them, when someone died he went down to Sheol, a kind of 'underworld' where the dead pass a drab, grey existence. There was no praise of God in Sheol; the life-line of the worshipping community had been cut. The singer of Psalm 102 drew some hope from his shared suffering with the community in Jerusalem — death would put an end to all that. Hezekiah again:

> For Sheol cannot praise you,
> nor Death celebrate you;
> those who go down to the pit
> can hope no longer in your constancy.
> The living, the living are the ones who praise you,
> as I do today. *Is 38:18-19*

For the Hebrews, to live is to praise; the rest is silence. Being distanced from God is the most terrifying effect of death. Psalm 88 describes this step-by-step 'descent into hell', beyond the memory of God:

> For my soul is filled with evils;
> my life is on the brink of the grave.
> I am reckoned as one in the tomb:
> I have reached the end of my strength,
> like one alone among the dead;
> like the slain lying in their graves;
> like those you remember no more,
> cut off, as they are, from your hand. *Ps 88:4-6* (see 6:5-6; 30:9-10)

In the face of this awful prospect, we seem to be quite helpless. All that we associate with life and good living are powerless against death: wealth, fame, power, health. . . . Rich or poor, good or bad, we must all die. Is there no hope, then? Must God, at the last, let go of all his creatures?

Psalm 49 is an attempt to grapple with this problem. There is a refrain that sums up the theme of the psalm:

In his riches, man lacks wisdom:
he is like the beasts that are destroyed. *vv 13 and 21*

It is not just that wealth and power can dehumanise us, and bring out the beast in us. Even more, we can forget that we must one day die, like any animal. Forget that

> All flesh is grass,
> and all its beauty is like the flower of the field.
> The grass withers, the flower fades. . . *Is 40:6-7a (RSV)*

If, then, the powerful are in the end so powerless, what of the poor who have no power at all?

vv 2-5
Formal introduction to this song in the style of a teacher of wisdom (compare Psalm 78:1ff). An indication of how weighty the matters to be dealt with are.

vv 6-13
The psalmist has nothing to fear from enemies who foolishly trust in their own wealth. They seem so well established now, so secure, but in the end death will sweep them away:

> For no man can buy his own ransom,
> or pay a price to God for his life.
> The ransom of his soul is beyond him.
> He cannot buy life without end,
> nor avoid coming to the grave. *vv 8-10*

The listeners, in agreement, sing the response (v 13).

vv 14-21
The singer seems to take a certain pleasure in describing the fate of the wicked as they are herded like sheep to the grave. Suddenly (and this is the pearl in this psalm) he claims that God will do for him what the rich cannot do: he will 'ransom me from death and take my soul to himself'. This is something quite new, and it is not clear exactly what the singer means. What is certain is that if God should 'take my soul to himself', then death is no longer a separation from God. Or rather, that God, stronger than death, will now allow the separation. The listeners again sing the response (v 21).

In Psalm 49, the psalmist's experience of injustice and inequality led him to a deeper understanding of death and of God. Psalm 73 reflects a similar experience and carries the conclusion even further.

Psalm 73 *With you, I am always with you*

1. How good God is to Israel, to those who are pure of heart!	THEME *of the psalm*
2. Yet my feet came close to stumbling, my steps had almost slipped 3. for I was filled with envy of the proud when I saw how the wicked prosper. 4. For them there are no pains; their bodies are sound and sleek. 5. They have no share in men's sorrows; they are not stricken like others. 6. So they wear their pride like a necklace, they clothe themselves with violence.	Experience of the singer: *He is faced* *with the problem of* *the wicked who* *prosper — Does God* *not see? Why should* *the good man bother* *to keep his heart pure* *when it seems to do* *him no good at all?*

7. Their hearts overflow with malice,
   their minds seethe with plots.
8. They scoff; they speak with malice;
   from on high they plan oppression.
9. They have set their mouths in the heavens
   and their tongues dictate to the earth.
10. So the people turn to follow them
    and drink in all their words.
11. They say: 'How can God know?
    Does the Most High take any notice?'
12. Look at them, such are the wicked,
    but untroubled, they grow in wealth.
13. How useless to keep my heart pure
    and wash my hands in innocence,
14. when I was stricken all day long,
    suffering punishment day after day.

15. Then I said: 'If I should speak like that,
    I should betray the race of your sons.'
16. I strove to fathom this problem,
    too hard for my mind to understand,
17. until I pierced the mysteries of God
    and understood what becomes of the wicked.
18. How slippery the paths on which you set them;
    you make them slide to destruction.
19. How suddenly they come to their ruin,
    wiped out, destroyed by terrors.
20. Like a dream one wakes from, O Lord,
    when you wake you dismiss them as phantoms.
21. And so when my heart grew embittered
    and when I was cut to the quick,
22. I was stupid and did not understand,
    no better than a beast in your sight.

Yet he remains faithful to God, and begins to understand his ways, and how brittle is the apparent prosperity of the wicked. They will not last; God will shrug them off.

The singer's bitterness at the injustice of life almost blinded him to the real insight:

23. Yet I was always in your presence;
    you were holding me by my right hand.
24. You will guide me by your counsel
    and so you will lead me to glory.
25. What else have I in heaven but you?
    Apart from you I want nothing on earth.
26. My body and my heart faint for joy;
    God is my possession for ever.
27. All those who abandon you shall perish;
    you will destroy all those who are faithless.
28. To be near God is my happiness.
    I have made the Lord God my refuge.
    I will tell of all your works
    at the gates of the city of Zion.

We are always in the presence of God. *The only worthwhile possession on earth or in heaven. And it does not end with death. This is a good news worth telling at the city gates!*

Psalm 73 represents a breakthrough from the traditional approach to the problem of injustice. Riches and power are indeed brought to an end by death, but that is small comfort to the poor man who must himself die in any case. In the psalm, the experience of the singer is described in vv 2-22. His envy of the rich at first tempted him to follow their ways (vv 2-14). He draws back from doing that, and reflects instead on the fleeting nature of wealth and the wealthy; but that too is an unsatisfactory attitude, and still poisoned by envy and bitterness (vv 15-22). No less than the rich man of the refrain in Psalm 49, the one who envies the rich is 'no better than a beast in your sight' (*Ps 73:22*). It is only by letting go of any desire for the world's riches that the singer is set free to find God. And finding God, he finds life. Death is not the ultimate fact — there is, now and always, the fact of God (vv 23-28). Life is not the absence of death but the presence of God. A modern version of Psalm 73:23-28 by Huub Oosterhuis expresses it well:

> With you, I am
> always with you.
> You hold me tight,
> your hand in mine.
> You will bring all things
> to a good end,
> you lead me on
> in your good pleasure.
> What is heaven
> to me without you,
> where am I on earth
> if you are not there?
> Though my body
> is broken down,
> though my heart dies,
> You are my Rock,
> my God, my future
> that waits for me.
>
> Far away from you
> life is not life.
> To break faith with you
> is to be no one.
>
> With you, my highest
> good, my God,
> with you I am
> secure.

Exercise 75: *Read and discuss (and if possible, enact) Psalm 73.*

In this psalm we have not only the experience of the psalmist, but his reflections on the effects of that experience on himself. Have you had any experiences in your life that have helped you face the question of death? Can you share with the group about such experiences, and what you have learned from them?

In all this, the psalmist and others were pushing at the barrier of death. They saw that God's power reaches even into Sheol (Psalm 139:8), that the love of God is better than life itself (Psalm 63:4), that God can snatch someone back from the very jaws of death (Psalms 28:1; 30:3-4). But when death does finally come, what then? Can it be that even beyond death we may still know and love God, praise him, be with him — for ever? In the last analysis, the psalmist hoped to be redeemed not just *from* death, but *through* death.

It was not until very near the time of Christ that these hopes were given a more solid form in the thinking of Israel, and even then only among certain groups. One of the factors that helped to establish these new insights was the need to redress the balance between the rich and the poor; if there was no justice in life, perhaps there would be in an 'after-life'? Thus the *Book of Daniel* (written about 165 BC):

> Of those who are sleeping in the Land of Dust, many will awaken, some to everlasting life, some to shame and everlasting disgrace. *Dn 12:2*

And the *Second Book of Maccabees* (about 124 BC) takes the resurrection of the body for granted. It was the great hope for those who were facing persecution and martyrdom: see chapter 7, and the words of a mother to the last of her seven children still to face a martyr's death:

> Do not fear this executioner, but prove yourself worthy of your brothers and accept death, so that I may receive you back with them in the day of mercy. *v 29*

Finally, barely fifty years before the birth of Christ, the *Book of Wisdom* speaks of immortality and eternal life with God as the reward for a good life:

> But the souls of the upright are in the hands of God,
> and no torment can touch them.
> To the unenlightened, they appeared to die,
> their departure was regarded as a disaster,
> their leaving us like an annihilation;
> but they are at peace.
> If, as it seemed to us, they suffered punishment,
> their hope was rich with immortality. . . . *3:1-4*

Belief in a resurrection to immortality was accepted by the Pharisees, but not by the Sadducees or the Samaritans. This was the way matters stood when Jesus came to face the mystery of his own death.

The death of Jesus

The New Testament writers are quite clear about the fact of Jesus' death, that he was aware of its coming, and that he was afraid of it. As the author of *Hebrews* put it:

> During his life on earth, he offered up prayer and entreaty, with loud cries and with tears, to the one who had the power to save him from death. . . . *5:7a*

In this he shared the experience of the psalmists and of all humanity. But Jesus was not trying or praying to avoid death — it was the whole purpose of his life to die:

> Now my soul is troubled.
> What shall I say:
> Father, save me from this hour?
> But it is for this very reason that I have come to this hour.
> Father, glorify your name! *Jn 12:27-28* (see Mark 14:32-42)

This is the kernel of Jesus' approach to death: it was the Father's will for him, something he had *to do*. He *gave* up his life, 'no one takes it from me; I lay it down of my own free will. . .' (see John 10:17-18). And so, because he died, because he shared in the mortality of all human beings, he could be raised from the dead. And this is the heart of the Gospel.

> I want to make quite clear to you, brothers, what the message of the gospel that I preached to you is. . . . The tradition I handed on to you in the first place, a tradition which I had myself received, was that Christ died for our sins, in accordance with the scriptures, and that he was buried; and that on the third day, he was raised to life, in accordance with the scriptures. . . *1 Co 15:1,3-4*

In this course we have already touched on the death and resurrection of Jesus from various aspects:

— Jesus completes the story of our salvation: he enters the emptiness of death and fills it with glory. In the long tale of God's care for us, death is the last enemy but not the final victor (see Chapter 2.6).

— The death of Jesus on the cross becomes the focal point of the grand forgiveness of Creation by its Maker: the severance of sin is healed and the world is redeemed from within (see Chapter 4.6).

— Jesus is the Messiah, the fulfilment of the hope of Israel. Even beyond that, he is himself a new range of hope, bringing us through death to a life we cannot yet imagine: we too live at the right hand of God (see Chapter 5.4).

— In his suffering Jesus shares in the broken state of our world; he stands with us in our darkest and most dreadful days (see Chapter 6.1).

Now, as a final exercise, I suggest an approach to the death of Jesus — and our own death — through his own sayings and stories.

Exercise 76:   *Ponder one or two of the passages proposed here. These could become the basis for shared insights and prayer in the group.*

(a) *In the death of Jesus, God has taken our greatest terror and turned it into a sign of his love for us:*
    No one can have greater love
    than to lay down his life for his friends.   Jn 15:13

(b) *As Jesus reminds us, the only answer to death is to die.*
    Unless a wheatgrain falls into the earth and dies, it remains only a single grain; but if it dies it yields a rich harvest.   Jn 12:24

(c) *The insight of Psalm 73 about the Presence of God is even more valid now:*
    Father,
    I want those you have given me
    to be with me where I am,
    so that they may always see my glory.   Jn 17:24

(d) *That, even so, death can be terrifying:*
    From the sixth hour there was darkness over all the land until the ninth hour. And about the ninth hour, Jesus cried out in a loud voice, 'Eli, eli, lama sabachthani?' that is, 'My God, my God, why have you forsaken me?'   Mt 27:45-46

(e) *Jesus changed the meaning of death by changing the meaning of life:*
    Jesus said (to Martha):
    'I am the resurrection.
    Anyone who believes in me, even though that person dies, will live, and whoever lives and believes in me
    will never die.
    Do you believe this?'   Jn 11:25-26

(f) *Dying should not just happen to us; it is something we must do.*
    Then, speaking to all, he said, 'If anyone wants to be a follower of mine, let him renounce himself and take up his cross every day and follow me. Anyone who wants to save his life will lose it; but anyone who loses his life for my sake, will save it.'   Lk 9:23-24